FITNESS AND NUTRITION: THE WINNING COMBINATION

Written by
Jane Buch
Home Economics teacher
Chippewa High School
Doylestown, Ohio

Illustrated by
Ric Snyder

Editor
Tate Baird

University Classics, Limited Publishers
Athens, Ohio 45701

Published by:
University Classics, Ltd.
Athens, Ohio 45701

Typesetting: Samantha Denney,
            University Classics, Ltd., Athens, OH
Printed by: BookCrafters, Chelsea, MI

Library of Congress Card Catalog Number: 84-51951
ISBN 0-914127-127-8 P/B
ISBN 0-914127-18-7 C/B
Third Edition
Reprinted 1995

Printed in the United States of America

TABLE OF CONTENTS

FORWARD

As a competitive marathon runner who qualified for the 1984 and 1988 Women's Olympic Marathon Trials, I have learned from personal experience about the importance of fitness and nutrition. In addition to my personal experiences, I have coached junior high, high school, and college track and cross country teams. I learned a lot about the concerns of young athletes from the questions they asked.

When I saw that teenage athletes wanted to learn more about the relationship of nutrition to their performance, I started teaching a home economics class called Athletic Nutrition. After I had taught this class for several years, my husband suggested that I write a book about athletics and nutrition especially for teenagers. This book, **Conditioning and Nutrition for Athletes: The Winning Combination**, was published in 1985. The purpose of this original book was to serve as a textbook to be used in high school sports nutrition classes. Special learning activites to use in class were included in an accompanying workbook. These activities were designed to help students apply what they had learned from reading the textbook.

Since 1985, there has been more interest in physical fitness and nutrition. Teenagers who may not be interested in competitive sports also want to learn about fitness and nutrition as a way to improve their appearance and health.

This revised edition of **Conditioning and Nutrition for Athletes: The Winning Combination** is the result of this growing interest in general fitness. While a large part of the book discusses athletic performance, more information has been included about basic fitness.

As in the original book, the revised edition makes references to the Activity Challenges in the accompanying workbook. If you are reading this book on your own rather than as a class textbook, keep in mind that it is not necessary to have the workbook. Although the workbook activities are helpful, it is not necessary to do the Activity Challenges to benefit from the information in the book.

New features in this revision are the Case Study at the beginning of each chapter and the Chapter Summary at the end. These Case Studies will give you the chance to *think*. When you can apply what you have learned and advise someone else, you should be able to use the information for your own situation.

Whether you are male or female, whether you choose to compete or not, the basic concepts of fitness and nutrition apply to everyone. The idea is to set your personal fitness and nutrition goals and then use what you have learned to meet these goals. Being healthy and fit for life is a good goal for all of us!

INTRODUCTION -- PART ONE

CONDITIONING FOR FITNESS
AND ATHLETIC PERFORMANCE

Good health is important for everyone. One way to achieve good health is to be physically fit. Physical fitness is important for good health throughout life. Heart disease, high blood pressure, back pain, and weight problems are partly caused by lack of exercise. These problems often begin early in life and may become life-threatening in adulthood. You are never too young to start a fitness program. You will also feel better and look better if you are physically fit. You will have more energy to lead an active life.

If you are an athlete, good health is also important to you. However, an athlete needs a higher level of physical fitness than someone who does not participate in sports. Competing in sports places extra stress and strain on your body. To meet the demands of athletic performance, you must spend even more time keeping your body in good condition. Achieving the high level of fitness needed for competition is called conditioning. While fitness is directed toward healthy, everyday living, conditioning is directed towards the specific demands of a sport. The more time and effort you put into a conditioning program, the more successful you will become.

The first four chapters of this book explain the key components of a general fitness or an athletic conditioning program. You will learn about stretching exercises to develop flexibility in Chapter One. Chapter Two explains how aerobic exercise helps develop a strong heart. The importance of strength training, which develops muscular power and endurance, is discussed in Chapter Three. Chapter Four will show you how to use these three key components to develop a complete general fitness or an athletic conditioning program to meet your personal needs and goals.

1 DEVELOPING FLEXIBILITY

CASE STUDY

I'm a sprinter and have had lots of problems with injuries. When I was in junior high, I pulled my right hamstring during a race. Since then, my right leg gets very sore whenever I run, and I'm afraid of pulling my hamstring again. What can I do to keep my leg from hurting?

--Terry, high school junior

Flexibility is the ability to move a joint and the tissues surrounding the joint through a full range of motion (ROM). Range of motion is influenced by the bones in the joint and the characteristics of the muscles, tendons, and ligaments surrounding the joint. The more movable a joint is, the more flexible it is. The natural degree of flexibility varies from one person to another. However, it is possible to increase flexibility by doing stretching exercises.

Flexibility is important for everyone. As a person grows older, flexibility can be lost rather quickly. If a person spends a lot of time sitting, backaches may be the result of inflexibility. Flexibility is even more important for athletes. All athletes depend on flexibility for prevention of injury and for optimum performance. Therefore, a regular stretching program should be included as part of a general fitness or an athletic conditioning program.

Joint Structures

To understand more about flexibility, you need to know about the structure of the joints in your body. At various places bones come together to form joints. Examples are the shoulder, elbow, wrist, hip, knee, and ankle joints. The joints contain ligaments, which connect bone to bone; they also contain tendons, which attach muscles to bones. The range of motion in each joint area is determined, in part, by the shape and structure of the bones in the joint. For example, the ball and socket structure of the shoulder joint is the most movable. This joint can move upward, downward, sideways, and in circular patterns. The knee, which is shown in Illustration 1-1, and the elbow are examples of hinge joints, which move only in two directions.

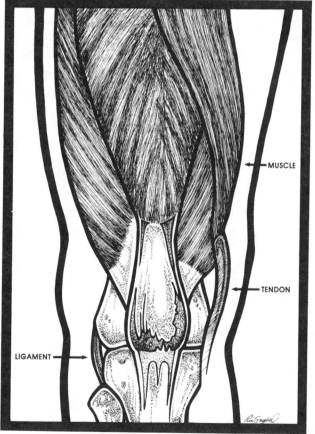

MUSCLE

TENDON

LIGAMENT

Illus. 1-1

KNEE JOINT – FRONT VIEW

The condition of the muscles in the joint areas also affects flexibility. When a joint is not used through its full range of motion, the muscles may shorten and become less flexible. This tightness may be caused either by old injuries or by disuse. Young people tend to be more flexible than adults, since their muscles have not shortened and tightened in the joint areas. Females usually are more flexible than males because their tendons and ligaments tend to be looser.

Evaluating Your Flexibility

How flexible are you? Specific tests have been developed to measure the range of motion of various joints in the body. A special instrument called a *goniometer* is used for these tests. A goniometer is a measuring device that is usually 12 to 16 inches long with two arms. One arm is stationary while the other arm moves to measure 0 to 180 degrees in each direction. A person with training in exercise physiology conducts these tests. The tester must use specific body positions and points on the body for the goniometer measurements to be accurate. Based upon the results of these tests, the degree of flexibility in the joints can be determined.

Other tests that do not require special laboratory procedures can be used to measure flexibility . The *Sit and Reach* and the *Prone Trunk Lift* tests can help you measure the flexibility of several important major muscle groups.

The Sit and Reach Test[1] is used to estimate the flexibility of the lower back and hamstrings. For this test you will need a sturdy wooden box about one foot high and a meter stick. Tape the meter stick to the top of the box so that 23 centimeters extend over the edge of the box toward you. Sit on the floor with the soles of your feet flat against the end of the box. Extend your arms forward. Then bend at the waist, reaching along the meter stick as far as you can.

The Prone Trunk Lift Test[2] estimates the flexibility of the upper back muscles. The only equipment needed is a meter stick. Lie face-down on the floor with your legs together and hands clasped

---

[1] AAHPERD. Health Related Physical Fitness Test Manual. Washington, D. C.: AAHPERD, 1980

[2] Getchell, L. Physical Fitness: A Way of Life. New York: John Wiley and Sons, 1979.

behind your neck. Have a partner kneel and straddle your legs, holding your buttocks down. Then lift your upper trunk (head and chest) as high off the floor as possible. Hold the highest position you can reach for three seconds. Have another partner use a meter stick to measure the distance from the floor to your chin. If you wish to take these tests, turn to Activity Challenge I in the workbook and carefully follow the directions for each test.

Importance of Flexibility

Many of our daily activities involve sitting at school or at work. Sitting for long periods causes many joints to be in a bent position much of the time, especially at the knee and hip. As a result the muscles around these joints may shorten. Shortened muscles limit movement in these joints and may lead to low back pain. Including stretching exercises in a general fitness program will often help prevent backaches.

Athletes require a higher degree of flexibility and flexibility requirements vary from sport to sport. Not all athletes need the high degree of flexibility that gymnasts and dancers must have. The development of flexibility is however important for all athletes. Athletes who are "tight" are more susceptible to muscle strains and tears. Sudden, jerky motions can cause injury. If an athlete is flexible, joints have a greater range of motion so that the muscles, tendons, and ligaments are not as easily strained or torn. Flexible muscles are also able to provide more power; muscle that has been lengthened through proper stretching can contract more forcefully to create more power. For these reasons, stretching exercises should be included as part of an athlete's conditioning program.

Stretching Methods

There are two ways to perform flexibility exercises: *active* stretching and *static* stretching. Active (ballistic) stretching uses five or six short, quick "bouncing" motions that pull on a muscle to stretch it. Although some athletes use active stretching, it is not the recommended method since the bouncing motion activates the stretch reflex system, which causes a muscle to become tighter. This stretch reflex action is caused by a feedback system operating between the muscle and the nervous system. Whenever you use a muscle, it contracts and relaxes. This cycle of contractions and relaxations is controlled by your brain and spinal cord. Tiny sensors in the muscle keep your nervous system informed about what that muscle is doing. When the muscle is stretched, the sensor is also stretched and sends a message back to the muscle to contract. How does this stretch reflex relate to bouncing when stretching? One type of these sensors reacts to sudden stretching. Each time you use a bouncing motion to stretch a muscle, it contracts in response to the forceful pull and sends a signal for the muscle to contract also. Therefore, your muscle is actually becoming shorter and tighter, rather than longer.

On the other hand, static stretching is characterized by using a slow, smooth motion to stretch a muscle. Slowly ease into the stretched position until you feel a slight "tension" in the muscle. You should be able to feel your muscles being stretched, but you should not feel any pain. Then hold this stretched position for 20 to 30 seconds. Static stretching is recommended for a variety of reasons. There is less danger of injury, especially if your muscles tend to be tight. Also, static stretching is less likely to cause muscle soreness; in fact, static stretching usually helps relieve muscle soreness. Most experts recommend static stretching as the best method for developing flexibility.

Developing and Maintaining Flexibility

To improve or maintain your flexibility, stretching exercises should be a regular part of your training program. Include stretching exercises as part of your warmup before any physical activity. The more intense the activity, the more important stretching becomes. These preliminary stretching exercises will help prevent muscle strains or tears. Your muscles will operate more efficiently since stretched muscles can contract more powerfully. Allow a minimum of 10 to 15 minutes for stretching in your warmup routine.

After an exercising or practicing session, you should stretch out again as part of your cooldown. At this time your muscles, tendons, and ligaments are warmer and more pliable. Therefore, they can be stretched more easily. Stretching while your muscles are warm will help to increase your flexibility. Be sure to stretch each joint and muscle group used during your activity. Taking 10 to 15 minutes to stretch immediately after exercise also will help prevent muscle tightness and soreness.

Stretching exercises are specific to a joint and surrounding tissues. For example, to develop flexibility in your shoulders, you must do stretching exercises that involve the shoulder joint and its surrounding muscles, tendons, and ligaments. Consider which joints and muscles are used most often in your activities. Which joints and muscles do you use most often for reaching, bending, and turning? Where are you likely to become sore after hard physical activity? The joints and muscles that you identify are the ones that should be stretched during warmup and cooldown.

There are many excellent exercises to use for improving or maintaining flexibility. A variety of exercises for different joint areas and muscle groups are described in this section. These exercises can be used as part of any fitness or conditioning program.

SHOULDERS

1. *Arm Rotations*
   Stand with the arms extended at sides, parallel with the ground.
   Beginning with large circles, rotate the arms in progressively smaller circles.
   Repeat rotations in opposite direction.

2. *Shoulder Stretch*
   While in a standing position, place the left hand over the left shoulder.
   Bring the right hand up behind the back and try to touch the fingertips of the right hand to the fingertips of the left hand.
   Repeat on opposite side.

CHEST AND BACK:

1. *Chest Stretch*
   In a standing position, hold arms out to the sides, parallel with the ground.
   Pull arms back until tightness is felt in the chest.

2. *Upper Back Stretch*
   In a standing position, hold arms out to the sides, parallel with the ground.
   Cross the arms in front of the chest until tightness is felt in the upper back.

ABDOMINALS:

1. *Trunk Rotations*
    Stand with feet about shoulder-width apart and with hand on hips.
    Twist at the waist as far as you can to the right, continuing to circle to the back, left, and front.
    Repeat complete rotation 3 to 5 times.
    Repeat rotations in opposite direction.

2. *Side Stretches*
    Stand with feet about shoulder-width apart and clasp hands behind head.
    Bend as far as you can to the right side.
    Repeat to left side.

HAMSTRINGS:

1. *Head to Knees (Standing)*
    Stand with the legs straddled wide and with the knees *slightly* bent.
    Using the hands for assistance, slowly bring the forehead to the right knee.
    Relax and repeat to the left side.

2. *Head to Knees (Seated)*
    Sit with the legs extended and together in front, with the knees *slightly* bent.
    Using the hands for assistance, bring the head down to touch knees.

3. *Modified Hurdler's Stretch* (See Illus. 1-2)
    Sit with legs extended in front. Then bring bottom of right foot to the inside of the left thigh.
    Using hands for assistance, bring head down to extended knee, keeping the extended knee *slightly* bent.
    Repeat to other side.

1. *Leg Curls*
    Stand, facing a wall, with left hand on wall for support and balance. Keep left leg *slightly* bent at knee.
    Bend the right knee and grasp the right ankle with the right hand.
    Pull right foot toward buttocks until tension is felt in the quadriceps.
    Repeat with the left leg.

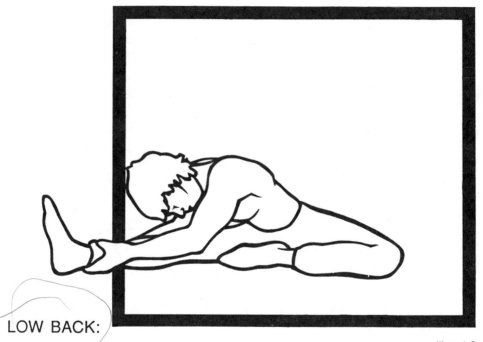

Illus. 1-2

LOW BACK:

1. *Knee to Chest*
    Lie on back with legs extended.
    Draw right knee up to the chest, with hands clasped around knee to assist in pulling knee tight against the chest.
    Keep left knee *slightly* bent.
    Repeat stretch with left leg.

2. *Double Knee to Chest*
   Lie on back with legs extended.
   Draw both knees up to the chest, with hands clasped around knees to assist in pulling knees tight against the chest.

HIPS:

1. *Hip Stretch*
   Lie on back with legs extended and hands clasped behind neck.
   Slide right leg up into a bent position so that the right foot is flat on the floor.
   Lift left leg over the right leg so that the legs are crossed at the knees. Then bend left leg at the knee.
   Keeping the right foot flat on the floor and pointed   straight ahead, use the left leg to pull the right leg left toward the floor.
   Keep shoulders, upper back, and head flat against the floor.

2. *Seated Hip Stretch*
   Sit on floor with legs extended.
   Cross left leg over right leg; then place left foot flat on floor next to right knee. (Left leg will be bent.) place right arm behind you on the floor.
   Support weight on right arm, keeping arm straight.
   Wrap left arm around left knee.
   Turn gently and look over right shoulder.
   Switch legs and repeat to opposite side.

LEG ADDUCTORS (GROIN):

1. *The Yogi*
   Sit with soles of the feet together and with the knees spread and flexed.
   Place hands on knees and press knees downward toward the floor to maximum stretch.

2. *Lunge*
   Assume a three-quarter squat position, with hands placed on floor in front of body.
   Extend right leg laterally to the right side.

9

Stretch by lowering hips until tension is felt in the groin area.
Repeat using left leg.

GASTROCNEMIUS-SOLEUS (CALF MUSCLES):

1. *Wall Push-Away* (See Illus. 1-3)
    Facing a wall, stand about two feet away with both feet pointing toward wall.
    Place right foot about 12 inches behind left foot.
    Bend left knee and lean into the wall, keeping heel of right foot on the ground and right knee locked. Continue to lean into the wall until you feel tension in the calf muscles.
    Repeat with left leg behind.

2. *Soleus Stretch*
    Assume the Wall Push-Away position, (as in Illus. 1-3), except bend the right knee instead of keeping it straight when leaning into the wall.
    Repeat with left leg, being sure to bend the left knee.

Illus. 1-3

10

ANKLE:

1. *Ankle Rotations*
    Sit with the right ankle crossed over the left knee. Using the hands for assistance, roll the right ankle in a clockwise direction 10 times.
    Then roll the right ankle in a counter-clockwise direction 10 times.
    Repeat with left ankle.

2. *Ankle Flexions/Extensions*
    Sit with the right ankle crossed over the left knee.
    Using the hands for assistance, point the toes of the right foot upward for 20 seconds.
    Then point the toes of the right foot downward for 20 to 30 seconds.
    Repeat with the left ankle.

Designing a Personal Flexibility Program

Now that you have learned about flexibility and stretching methods and exercises, you are ready to design a flexibility program to meet your own personal needs.

The results of your Sit and Reach and the Prone Trunk Lift tests should help you to determine the goals for your flexibility program. Do you need to maintain your present level of flexibility or do you need to improve your flexibility? If you wish to develop a high degree of flexibility, you will need to spend more time stretching than if you wish only to maintain flexibility. To develop flexibility it is necessary to hold stretches longer or to repeat an exercise several times. The amount of time you spend on your flexibility program also will be determined by your natural degree of flexibility and the amount of flexibility needed for your activities and sports.

Determine which joints and muscles are used most often in your activities. Then for your warmup and cooldown include exercises that stretch each of these joints and muscles.

Stretching should be a non-competitive activity. You should not compare your ability to do stretching exercises with someone else since the natural degree of flexibility varies from one person to another. Also, remember that flexibility can vary from one side of the body to the other and from one joint to the other. When doing stretching exercises, determine the "comfort zone" of motion for

11

each joint. There should be no pain when you stretch. You should feel only a slight tension so that you know the muscles being stretched. Then work to gradually increase the range of motion for each joint. Activity Challenge II in the workbook will help you complete your flexibility program.

CHAPTER SUMMARY--CASE STUDY

Re-read the Case Study that introduced this chapter. Using the information in this chapter, what advice would you give Terry?

1. Why does Terry's right leg get sore?

2. Why is it important for Terry to develop flexibility, especially in the hamstrings?

3. What type of stretching method do you recommend for Terry?
    Why do you recommend this type of stretching?

4. When is the best time for Terry to do stretching exercises? Explain the reasons for your recommendation.

5. What stretching exercises would you recommend for Terry?

2 AEROBIC CONDITIONING

CASE STUDY

I play basketball on the junior varsity team. I'm a good foul shooter and can rebound well. My problem is that I get tired easily, especially during the fourth quarter of a game. Coach always has us do wind sprints at the beginning of practice, so I decided to do another ten minutes of wind sprints after practice. I thought this would make me stronger, but I'm almost as tired as I was before. What can I do so that I have more energy during the last minutes of the game?

--Chris, high school sophomore

Of all the key fitness components, *aerobic conditioning* (also known as *cardiovascular conditioning*) is the most important. All cells in the body need a continuous supply of oxygen in order to function. Aerobic conditioning improves the ability of the heart and lungs to supply oxygen to the cells. As the heart and lungs become stronger more oxygen can be transported throughout the body. With more oxygen the body can function with less fatigue during everyday activities.

Aerobic exercise also has other benefits. One benefit is lowering the levels of cholesterol found in the blood. If fatty deposits build up and clog the arteries, a heart attack can result. Aerobic exercise is also one of the most effective forms of weight control. Therefore, aerobic conditioning is important to everyone for general fitness and good health.

An athlete must be in even better condition aerobically than the average person. During intense physical activities, the cells in the muscles need even more oxygen to produce energy. When the muscle cells do not get enough oxygen, fatigue is the result. Aerobic conditioning increases the body's ability to produce energy. If the heart and lungs can supply enough oxygen to meet the increased demands of exercise, the muscles can work longer and harder with less effort and fatigue.

The Oxygen Transport System

There are two systems that work together to form the body's oxygen transport system. The *respiratory system* is composed of the air passages and the lungs. The heart and the blood vessels make up the *circulatory system*.

Let's take a tour through the oxygen transport system. (shown in Illustration 2-1). As you inhale, air enters the mouth and nose. In your throat, the air then passes down through the trachea, which branches into two passages called bronchial tubes. The bronchial tubes lead into each lung. At the end of the bronchial tubes are tiny air sacs, which are called alveoli. Blood circulating through the lungs flows past the alveoli. Oxygen then passes through the walls of the alveoli and into the blood stream where it combines with hemoglobin. Hemoglobin, which is found in red blood cells, acts as a magnet to attract oxygen. The oxygen then travels with the blood to the heart. As the heart beats, the oxygen-rich blood is pumped through the arteries to the capillaries in the muscles. Here the oxygen is freed from the hemoglobin and passes into the muscle cells to be used for energy production.

The process is then reversed. When the cells produce energy, carbon dioxide is created and must be eliminated. The carbon dioxide attaches to hemoglobin which has released the oxygen it was carrying. Carbon dioxide is carried in the blood through the veins back to the heart. The heart pumps the returning blood to the lungs and the carbon dioxide is released when you exhale. The process then begins once again, with the blood picking up more oxygen to be carried throughout the body.

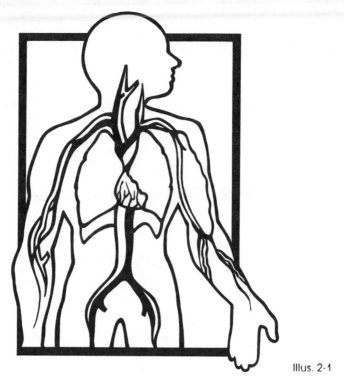

Illus. 2-1

Pulse as an Indicator of Aerobic Fitness

You can determine how strong your heart is by learning more about pulse rate and how to use it as a measure of cardiovascular fitness. You can find your heart rate by counting your pulse, which is the movement of blood through the arteries. To take your pulse, locate the radial artery on the inner side of one of your wrists or one of the carotid arteries in your neck. Place your first two fingers (do not use your thumb, since it contains its own pulse) over the selected artery, feeling for the pulses of blood. Using a watch, count the number of pulses you feel in 30 seconds and multiply by two, thus obtaining your resting pulse rate. Illustration 2-2 shows this procedure for taking the radial pulse. Practice locating and counting your pulse several times so that you can take your pulse easily and accurately.

A true resting pulse rate is one which is taken in the morning before you get out of bed. For an accurate estimate of your resting pulse rate, take your pulse for five days in the morning before getting up. To figure your resting pulse rate, add these five morning pulse readings and divide by five. The average resting pulse rate for an untrained person averages between 70 and 80 beats per minute. For highly conditioned athletes, resting pulse rates may be as low as 40 beats per minute. As your level of aerobic fitness improves, your resting pulse rate should become lower.

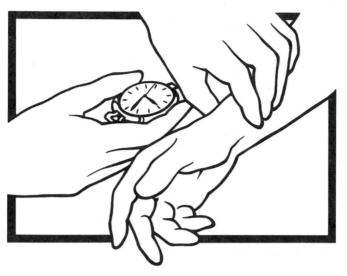

Recovery rate after exercise is also influenced by your degree of cardiovascular fitness. During physical activity, the muscles need more oxygen to work and produce energy. To meet this added demand, the heart pumps more blood to the muscles by beating faster. After stopping activity, the heart begins to slow down (recover) in approximately one minute. The more conditioned your heart is, the more quickly your pulse returns to its normal resting rate.

To see how your heart responds to exercise and how it recovers, turn to Activity Challenge I in your workbook.

Meeting Increased Oxygen Demands

As you have read, muscles need more oxygen during physical exertion to produce energy. This demand can be met in one of two ways. The heart can pump more blood to the working muscles by beating faster, or the heart can push more blood through the arteries with each beat. Since the heart is a muscle, it responds to aerobic exercise by growing stronger. As you become more fit, your heart is able to do the same amount of work with less effort. It can pump a larger volume of blood to the muscles with each beat. Therefore, the *stroke volume* of the heart is improved, and more oxygen is transported to the working muscles. More oxygen means more endurance and less fatigue.

Determining Your Level of Aerobic Fitness

Before starting a program to develop aerobic fitness, it's a good idea see how aerobically fit you are. There are several tests that can be used to assess cardiovascular fitness levels. The most accurate testing procedure is conducted in an exercise physiology laboratory using sophisticated and expensive equipment. This test, which is called a *VO$_2$ Max Test*, requires that you run on a treadmill or ride a stationary bicycle. By using a special mouthpiece for breathing, the air that is inhaled and exhaled is closely monitored. A computerized machine analyzes the amount of oxygen that is taken in by the blood as it passes through the lungs and is transported to the working muscles. The maximal amount of oxygen that can be used by the muscles is called VO$_2$ Max.

The VO$_2$ Max for normally active young males is about 44 to 47 milliliters of oxygen per kilogram of body weight per minute. A trained athlete will be able to use more oxygen and will have a higher VO$_2$ Max reading. For example, an Olympic marathon runner may have a VO$_2$ Max reading of over 70. For normally active young females, the average VO$_2$ Max is approximately 40 milliliters of oxygen per kilogram of bodyweight per minute. A very highly trained female endurance athlete may have a VO$_2$ Max reading of over 60. The difference in VO$_2$ Max readings between males and females is because males have a larger heart than females. A larger heart produces a greater stroke volume so that more oxygen can be delivered to the working muscles.

Since it is impractical for most people to take a VO$_2$ Max test, several other tests have been devised to estimate aerobic fitness. One method to evaluate aerobic fitness levels is to use runs of various times or distances. These tests are based on the idea that the distance run in a designated time is determined by the ability to maintain a certain level of oxygen intake and use. A test of this type is the *12 Minute Test*, which was developed by Dr. Kenneth Cooper. The object of this test is to walk, jog, or run as far as possible in 12 minutes. Another similar test is the *1.5 Mile Run*

Test [3]. For this test you time how long it takes to walk, jog, or run 1.5 miles. Fitness rating charts based on distance completed or time required to complete a distance have been developed to give an aerobic fitness rating category. Accurate results depend upon establishing a good pace for the test. It is important to walk or run at a *steady* pace that you think you can maintain throughout the entire test. Some people start too fast and are forced to slow down towards the end of the test or even stop before the test is over. Others may walk or run too slowly. As a result, test scores may be lower due to pacing errors. If you would like to use the 1.5 Mile Run Test to determine your level of aerobic fitness, turn to Activity Challenge II in the workbook and carefully follow the testing procedure.

Requirements for Aerobic Exercise

What types of exercise meet the requirements for aerobic conditioning? Aerobic means "with oxygen." Therefore, aerobic exercise must be done at a continuous, steady pace so that the heart can supply sufficient oxygen to the working muscles. To be classified as an aerobic exercise, the activities you select must meet the following requirements:

FREQUENCY-- The activity must be done at least three or four times each week to strengthen the cardiovascular system.

DURATION-- The activity must be done continuously for 20 to 30 minutes during each exercise session.

INTENSITY-- The activity must raise the pulse into the target zone for the duration of each exercise session. The target zone is considered to be 70 to 80% of your maximal heart rate (MHR).

To calculate your target zone for aerobic exercise, use the following formula:

---

[3] Cooper, Kenneth. The Aerobics Way. New York: M. Evans Company, 1977.

Step 1:   Determine your maximal heart rate (MHR) by subtracting your age from 220.

$$220 - \underline{\hspace{1cm}} \text{ (age)} = \underline{\hspace{2cm}} \text{ (MHR)}$$

Step 2:   Determine your target zone by calculating 70-80% of your MHR.

$$\text{MHR} \times .70 = \text{low end of target zone}$$
$$\text{MHR} \times .80 = \text{upper end of target zone}$$

Effective aerobic exercises use a large number of major muscle groups. Some excellent aerobic activities are walking, jogging, running, bicycling,rowing, and aerobic dance. Aerobic exercise should be done at a steady pace. As a result, the muscles can get all the oxygen they need to work continuously throughout the activity. A good way to tell if you are exercising aerobically is to use the "talk-test." If you can carry on a conversation with a partner while you are exercising and are not out of breath, you are supplying your muscles with a sufficient supply of oxygen.

Do not confuse aerobic exercises with anaerobic activities. *Anaerobic* is the opposite of aerobic. Anaerobic means "without oxygen." Anaerobic activities require an all-out effort of short duration. For example, running can be done either aerobically or anaerobically. If you run at a conversational pace that you can maintain for 20 to 30 minutes, you are exercising aerobically. However, if you are doing "wind-sprints," you are running as hard as you can for 10 to 20 seconds. Then you stop to "catch your breath" before doing another wind-sprint. When you exercise anaerobically, your heart cannot supply enough oxygen to the working muscles. You cannot exercise long without oxygen, so you need frequent "recovery" periods to allow your muscles to recover from oxygen debt. Oxygen debt also causes a waste product called lactic acid to build up in your muscles. Your muscles can tolerate only small amounts of lactic acid. If you accumulate large amounts of lactic acid, you will experience muscle pain and fatigue.

Anaerobic exercise will not strengthen your heart as effectively as aerobic exercise. When you exercise anaerobically, the result is a cycle of too much-too little. Although your heart rate will usually rise to the upper end of your target zone, it does not remain in the target zone long enough for the oxygen transport system to be strengthened.

When selecting activities for aerobic exercise, choose exercises and activities that are done continuously at a steady pace rather than "stop-start" activities. Participating in games such as volleyball and softball does not promote improvement in aerobic fitness. These activities do not require constant movement and do not keep the heart rate in the target zone long enough for aerobic conditioning to take place.

Designing an Aerobic Fitness Program

Now that you have learned about the importance of aerobic fitness, you are ready to design your own aerobic conditioning program. First, you will need to determine your goals.

For athletes, a strong oxygen transport system forms the base for all other conditioning activities. In an athletic conditioning program, goals are "sport specific." The level of aerobic fitness you need depends on the requirements of your sport. Athletes competing in sports such as long-distance running, swimming, and cycling, must have higher aerobic fitness goals than athletes participating in sports such as volleyball and baseball/softball. An athlete who needs to develop a high level of aerobic conditioning must exercise more often, longer, and harder than an athlete who needs a minimum level of aerobic fitness. For example, a cross-country runner may run six days a week for 30 to 40 minutes at 80% of maximal heart rate to develop a high degree of aerobic fitness. In contrast, a baseball player might run three days a week for 20 minutes at 70% of maximal heart rate.

In a general fitness program, goals are related to overall good health. Your main goal for an aerobic fitness program should be to develop a strong heart. A strong heart can function more efficiently and will not have to work as hard as a weak heart. If you begin an aerobic exercise program when you are young, you can reduce the chance of heart disease later in life. Exercising aerobically helps lower the amount of fat found in the blood. The chance of having a heart attack is reduced, since the arteries are less likely to become clogged. Aerobic exercise is also one of the best ways to help you maintain a desirable weight. Most persons who participate in an aerobic fitness program will tell you that they not only feel better, but also look better.

After determining your goals, you should then consider what exercises you will use for your conditioning or fitness program. The main consideration is to select exercises that meet the requirements of intensity, duration, and frequency. Also choose activities that you enjoy so that you will not be as likely to quit after a week or two. Instead of using only one type of aerobic exercise, you might wish to use a combination of exercises to prevent boredom and injury.

For a general fitness program, many persons have found that one of the best aerobic exercises is walking. The obvious difference between walking and jogging is speed. Another difference is that there is less pounding with walking. Lower speed and less impact reduce the likelihood of injury during exercise. This is especially important if you are just beginning a aerobic exercise program.

A walking program should also be designed around the principles of intensity, duration, and frequency. A good place to start is to walk at a brisk, "conversational pace" for 20 minutes three times a week. When this becomes easy, you can walk faster (intensity), walk for 30 minutes (duration), or walk five times a week (frequency). You can also make walking more difficult by swinging your arms vigorously or by using hand weights.

For athletes who are recovering from injury, walking is a good way to maintain aerobic fitness. Walking can also help promote healing since it increases blood flow to the injured muscles throughout the body.

Activity Challenge III in the workbook will help you follow the guidelines discussed in this chapter as you develop a personal aerobic fitness or conditioning program.

CHAPTER SUMMARY--CASE STUDY

Re-read the Case Study that introduced this chapter. Using the information in this chapter, what advice would you give Chris?

1. Why does Chris become fatigued during the fourth quarter of a game?

2. Why didn't the extra ten minutes of wind sprints help Chris to build endurance?
   What type of exercise is a wind sprint?

3. What type of exercise would you recommend for Chris to build endurance?

Explain how this type of exercise builds endurance.

4. Discuss the three requirements for aerobic exercise.

5. How will an aerobic exercise program help Chris maintain good health later in life

3 STRENGTH TRAINING

CASE STUDY

I've been wrestling in the 112 pound weight class, but I've had trouble keeping my weight down. So, next year I plan to wrestle in a higher weight class. I know I need to add muscle and build strength to wrestle at 119 pounds. What type of weight training program should I use? Should I use protein supplements or steroids to gain weight and strength faster?

--Jon, high school sophomore

Muscular fitness involves the skeletal muscles, which are attached in pairs to the bones. There are more than 215 pairs of skeletal muscles in the body; each pair of skeletal muscles work together to move the body by contracting and relaxing. By using the skeletal muscles you control the movement of your body.

Since our daily activities require pulling, pushing, and lifting motions, muscular fitness is important for everyone. Besides helping you perform daily activities with less fatigue, muscular fitness is also important for good health and appearance. Strong abdominal and back muscles can help prevent back pain. Well-defined and toned muscles give the body a better appearance. Athletes require a higher level of muscular fitness since they are placing even greater demands on their bodies. A well-designed strength training program will help you meet your goals for personal fitness and athletic performance.

Defining Muscular Fitness

Muscular fitness involves strength and endurance of the skeletal muscles. **Muscular strength** is the maximum amount of force that a muscle can produce in a single effort. A power lifter who is attempting to lift 500 pounds requires a high degree of muscular strength. In contrast, **muscular endurance** is the ability of a muscle to repeat the same motion over and over. Performing sit-ups or push-ups requires muscular endurance.

Which is more important, strength or endurance? The amount of strength and endurance you need depends upon your activities. Football linemen and competitors in the shot-put and discus rely mainly on strength. Strength is also important for sprinters in running, swimming, and cycling events. On the other hand, muscular endurance is critical for distance runners, swimmers, and cyclists. Other sports involve both muscular strength and endurance. Wrestling is a good example of a sport requiring a combination of strength and endurance. Strength is used to apply a hold, but endurance is used to maintain the hold. Muscular fitness can help all athletes improve their performances. They will experience less fatigue and muscle soreness. You are also less likely to suffer muscular injuries such as strains and sprains.

Muscle Composition

In order to understand how strength is developed, let's take a look at the composition of the skeletal muscles. A single muscle is composed of many long, thin cells called fibers. There are two types of fibers, fast-twitch fibers and slow-twitch fibers. **Fast-twitch** fibers develop more power, but tire quickly. **Slow-twitch** fibers don't develop as much power, but they can work for a longer period of time without becoming tired.

Fast-twitch fibers are used in short-term activities such as the 100 meter dash. Slow-twitch fibers are suited for long-term activities such as marathon running. However, most activities and sports use both types of muscle fibers.

A test called a muscle biopsy can be performed to determine the percentage of fast-twitch and slow-twitch fibers found in the muscles of the arms or legs. The area where the biopsy is to be taken is numbed. Then a scalpel is used to make a small incision through the skin and outer tissue of the muscle. A biopsy needle is inserted into the incision and is pushed into the belly of the muscle. A small plunger, which is pushed through the center of the needle, snips off a small sample of muscle tissue. The sample is removed from the needle, cleaned, and quickly frozen. It is then thinly sliced, stained, and examined under a microscope. By counting the stained cells, the number of fast-twitch and slow-twitch fibers can be determined. The average person has about 50% fast-twitch fibers and 50% slow-twitch fibers. It is not uncommon for outstanding sprinters to have about 75% fast-twitch fibers and 25% slow-twitch fibers. On the other hand, elite marathon runners would be more likely to have 25% fast-twitch fibers and 75% slow-twitch fibers. Since the ratio of fast-twitch fibers to slow-twitch fibers is determined by heredity, there is little you can do to alter the fiber composition of your muscles. Therefore, some persons are born to be better sprinters than marathoners.

Becoming Stronger

How you become stronger? *Strength training* causes improvement to take place in the muscle fibers that you already have. When you work to develop muscular fitness, the muscles undergo changes in response to the extra work they are forced to do. One change is that the muscle fibers get larger. This increase in muscle size is called *hypertrophy*. Another change is that more muscle fibers may be recruited into use when the muscle is forced to work harder. As the muscle fibers increase in size and more fibers are used, the muscle becomes stronger. Training will not change the ratio of fast-twitch to slow-twitch muscle fibers that you have. Nor will strength training increase the number of muscle fibers you have. However, the existing muscle fibers are enlarged and strengthened.

Women and Strength Training

Strength training is also important for women. In the past women avoided weight training because they thought they would develop huge, bulky muscles. They feared that developing muscles would make them look unfeminine. However, in recent years research has shown that women can gain strength without large increases in muscle bulk.

There are several reasons that women generally do not develop large muscles during strength training. In order for muscle fibers to increase in size, the male hormone, *testosterone*, must be present. Testosterone is present in both males and females. Usually, females do not have enough testosterone to produce large increases in muscle fiber size. However, the level of testosterone varies from one woman to the other. Those women with higher testosterone levels may build more muscle bulk than women with lower testosterone levels.

The size of muscle fibers also affects the degree of muscle hypertrophy in females. Men and women have muscle fibers that are similar in composition, but the size of the muscle fibers in women is smaller. Therefore, women are not able to develop the large muscle mass that men can.

Female athletes now realize that strength training improves performance. It has become a part of their over-all conditioning program to increase strength and prevent injuries. Many women who exercise for health and fitness have also discovered strength training. For them, strength training is a way to improve appearance by toning the muscles.

Measuring Muscular Fitness

Many tests have been developed to measure muscular strength and endurance. Several of these tests are easy to take and give reliable estimates of one's strength and endurance.

The *dominant grip test* uses an instrument called a *dynamometer* to measure the strength of your dominant hand. The dynamometer has a handle which is connected to one end of a steel spring. The other end of the spring is attached to a pointer which moves along a scale of numbers. To use the dynamometer, hold it in your dominant hand and squeeze the handle as hard as you can. The force you apply compresses the steel spring and moves the pointer along the scale. The dynamometer will measure your grip strength in kilograms. Charts have been developed to indicate ratings of excellent, good, fair, etc. based upon grip strength and sex.

Another way to determine strength of various muscles is to use a method called the *one-repetition maximum test 1-RM*. This refers to the maximum amount of weight that can be lifted one time for a selected weight-lifting exercise. For the 1-RM test requires a barbell and weights or weight machines. First, choose a lifting exercise that will use the muscle group you want to test. Then select a suitable starting weight close to but below what you feel is the maximum you can lift. If you complete one repetition, add additional weight until you can no longer perform one lift. Weight is usually added in 10, 5, or 2½ pound increments. The last weight at which you could perform one complete lift is your one-lift maximum. Charts have been designed to indicate strength ratings for males and females based upon body weight and the amount of weight lifted for several weight lifting exercises.

To measure muscular endurance as well as strength, pull-ups can be used to test the arm and shoulder muscles. The only equipment required for this test is a horizontal bar about 1½ inches in diameter placed high enough so that you can hang without your feet touching the floor. Grasp the bar with an overhand grip (palms away from the body). Assume a hanging position with arms and legs fully extended. Your feet should not touch the floor. Raise your body using your arms until your chin is just above the bar. Then lower your body to the full hang of the starting position. Do not kick your legs for momentum. Repeat the pull-ups as many times as possible. Count the number of properly performed pull-ups you are able to complete. You can then use a rating chart to determine your level of muscular fitness.

Bent-knee sit-ups can be used to test the endurance level of the abdominal muscles, which are important for supporting and maintaining posture. Lie on your back with knees flexed and feet flat on the floor. Your heels should be about 12 to 18 inches from the buttocks. Have a partner hold your feet flat on the floor. Cross your arms over your chest, placing your hands on opposite shoulders. Then curl up into a sitting position so that the elbows touch the thighs. Return to the starting position with the back on the floor. This counts as one completed sit-up. You should perform as many sit-ups as possible for 60 seconds. As with the other tests, you can find your rating for this test on specially developed charts.

You may want to try some of these tests to measure your level of muscular fitness. Your local YMCA or YWCA may have fitness testing programs to test muscular fitness. Activity Challenge I in the workbook also contains testing procedures and rating charts for the hand grip, pull-up and sit-up tests.

Principles of Strength Training

Just any old exercises won't develop strength. In order for a *strength training program* to be of benefit, you cannot use a haphazard approach. Regardless of whether you want to train to develop muscular strength or muscular endurance, you should follow the basic principles that are discussed in this section.

1. *PRINCIPLE OF SPECIFICITY*:
   To develop strength, you must work the specific muscles that you want to develop. For example, to develop the biceps, you must exercise the biceps. The more similar the strength training exercises are to the actions used in your daily activities and sports, the more effective your training program becomes.

2. *PRINCIPLE OF OVERLOAD*:
   The only way you can improve strength is to make the muscles do more work than normal. This is called *overloading*. Overloading can be done in one of two ways.
   By increasing intensity--To increase intensity you would lift heavier weights. Because it is harder to lift heavier weights, you would be able to perform an exercise fewer times. Increasing intensity helps develop muscular strength.
   By increasing duration--To increase duration you would lift lighter weights so that you can increase the number of times you perform an exercise. Increasing duration helps develop muscular endurance.

3. *PRINCIPLE OF PROGRESSION*:
   For a conditioning program to be of real benefit, you should gradually and continually increase the workload. It does not take long for your body to adapt to the initial overload. If you want to continue improving your level of fitness, you must increase the workload. For example, when you started to lift, bench pressing 150 pounds was difficult. However, a few weeks later, lifting 150 pounds became easy because your strength had increased. If you want to continue improving strength, you would increase the workload to 160 pounds.

Isotonic Exercise

Isotonic exercises can be used to develop both muscular strength and endurance. Isotonic exercise involves performing a normal body motion while adding resistance. As the motion is performed, the muscle shortens and lengthens through its full range of motion. The added resistance can be either a part of the body or another object. A simple example of an isotonic exercise is to hold a soup can in your hand as you raise and lower your arm several times. Weight lifting is a popular form of isotonic exercise for developing muscular strength and endurance. A strength training program may include calisthenics that use body weight as the resistance or lifting exercises that use weights in the form of barbells, dumbbells, and pulleys.

Illus. 3-1

Weight Training Equipment

What kinds of equipment do you need for a strength training program? Calisthenics, which use body weight as the resistance, require little or no extra equipment. Body-weight calisthenics such as sit-ups and push-ups are convenient since they can be done almost anywhere.

Weight lifting exercises can be done with a variety of free weights. Dumbbells range in weight from 2 pounds to 75 pounds or more. Olympic barbells usually weigh 45 pounds. Weight plates can be added to raise the weight to well over 200 pounds.

Weight machines such as the Universal Gym can also be used for weight training. These machines have stacks of graduated weights that are adjusted with pins to the proper setting. The weight stack is then lifted by cables as you apply force against a bar. Nautilus makes specially designed machines with cams and counterweights for variable resistance.

Which type of equipment gives the best results, free weights or weight machines? Each type has advantages and disadvantages. For example, one of the advantages of free weights is that they help develop balance since you must support the weight yourself. A disadvantage is that, for safety purposes, you should always have a spotter working with you. Weight machines provide the advantage of being easier to make adjustments in the weight since all you have to do is change the position of a pin. Another advantage is that a spotter is not necessary since the weights are supported for you.

Experts on weight training agree that it is not the equipment but the effort that you put into your weight training program that gives the desired results. A combination of free weights and weight machines usually gives excellent results.

Strength Training Exercises

What kinds of exercises can be used to develop muscular strength and endurance? This section contains descriptions of some of the calisthenics and weight lifting exercises you could include in an over-all strength training program.

BODY-WEIGHT CALISTHENICS:

1. *Push-Ups*
   Lie face down on the floor.

Place hands on floor next to shoulders.
Keep legs and body straight while you push up until your arms are extended and fully straight. Lower yourself until your chin touches the floor.
Repeat.

2. *Pull-Ups*
   Hang from a bar high enough so that your feet do not touch the floor. Grasp the bar with the palms of your hands facing away from your body. Slowly pull your chin up and over the bar. Don't swing or kick.
   Lower yourself to the starting position so that your arms are straight.
   Repeat.

3. *Sit-Ups*
   Lie on your back with arms crossed on your chest.
   Bend knees at a 90 degree angle. Keep feet flat on floor.
   Slowly curl up into a sitting position and touch your elbows to your knees. Slowly roll back down to the starting position.
   Repeat.

4. *Abdominal Curls*
   Lie on your back with arms crossed on your chest.
   Bend knees at a 90 degree angle. Keep feet flat on floor.
   Curl upper trunk and head off the floor as far as possible but do not do a full sit-up. Slowly roll back down to the starting position.
   Repeat.

5. *Prone Trunk Lift*
   Lie face down on floor.
   Clasp hands behind neck.
   Slowly lift your head and chest off the floor.
   Lower upper body to starting position.
   Repeat.

6. *Side Leg Raise*
   Lie on your right side, using your arms for balance.
   Lift your left leg straight up from your side as high as you can.
   Slowly lower your leg to the starting position and repeat.
   Roll over and repeat lifts with your right leg.

WEIGHT LIFTING EXERCISES

1. *Bench Press*:
   To strengthen muscles of chest, shoulders, and triceps

   Equipment: Barbell, exercise bench, and rack or exercise machine

   Starting Position and Movement:
   Lie on your back on the exercise bench with knees bent and feet flat on the floor.
   Place hands on bar with palms upward, slightly wider than shoulder width.
   Remove the barbell from the rack. Hold the weight above your chest with your arms fully extended. Then slowly lower the weight to your chest. Push the weight up until your arms are fully extended once again. (One repetition.)

   NOTE: Always have a spotter for this exercise when using a barbell.

2. *Seated Shoulder Press*:
   To strengthen the muscles of the shoulder and triceps.

   Equipment: Barbell and exercise bench or exercise machine

   Starting Position and Movement:
   Sit on an exercise bench. Position the bar so that it rests on the shoulders behind the neck. Raise the weight so that the arms are fully extended and then slowly lower the weight to the starting position. (One repetition.)

3. *Upright Rowing*:
   To strengthen the muscles of the upper back, shoulders and biceps.

   Equipment : Barbell or exercise machine

   Starting Position and Movement:
   Stand with feet shoulder width apart. Hold the bar in both hands with palms on top, a little closer than shoulder-width

apart. The arms should be fully extended downward. Pull the weight up until the bar touches your chin. Do not use your legs or back to help with the lifting. Slowly lower the weight to the starting position. (One repetition.)

4. *Shrug*:
   To strengthen the muscles of the upper back and shoulders.

   Equipment: Barbell or exercise machine

   Starting Position and Movement:
   Stand with feet shoulder width apart. Hold bar in both hands with palms on top, a little farther than width apart. The arms should be fully extended downward with the shoulders relaxed. Raise shoulders as high as possible. Do not bend the arms when raising the weight. Lower shoulders to the starting position. (One repetition.)

5. *Biceps Curl*:
   To strengthen the biceps.

   Equipment: Barbell or exercise machine

   Starting Position and Movement:
   Hold the bar in both hands, palms facing up. Arms should be extended downward. Raise the bar to your chest by bending your arms. Keep your elbows locked at your sides. Do not use your legs or arch your back. Slowly lower the bar to the starting position. (One repetition.)

6. *Triceps Extension*:
   To strengthen the triceps.

   Equipment: Lat machine

   Starting Position and Movement:
   Stand facing the bar. Grasp the bar with palms of hands away from the body. Hands should be placed about shoulder width apart. Pull the bar down to neck level.   Pull elbows in tight against the rib cage. Press the weight down, moving the lower arm only until the arms are fully extended. Slowly return to the starting position.   (One repetition.)

7. *Wrist Curls:*
To strengthen the muscles in the forearm.

Equipment: Barbell or dumbbells and exercise bench

Starting Position and Movement:
Sit on exercise bench with feet flat on the floor. Grasp the bar with palms upward. Place the forearms on the thighs, with the back of the hands against the knees. Flex the wrists, raising the weight upward. Be sure the forearm and elbow remain in contact with the thigh. Lower weight to the starting position. (One repetition.)
To perform a reverse curl, grasp the bar with the palms downward. Complete the movement of raising and lowering the weight as described above.

8. *Lat Pulldown*:
To strengthen the Latissimus dorsi (musculature of the middle back.

Equipment: Lat machine

Starting Position and Movement:
Assume a sitting or kneeling position on the floor in front of the bar. Grasp the bar at each end with the palms of your hands away from you. Pull the bar downward to the base of the neck. Slowly allow the bar to return to the starting position (One repetition.)
For a variation on the above exercise, grasp the bar with the palms of your hands facing your body, shoulder width apart. Pull the bar downward until it touches the upper part of your chest. Slowly return to the starting position. (One repetition.)

9. *Side Bends*:
To strengthen the muscles of the trunk.

Equipment: Dumbbells

Starting Position and Movement:

Stand with feet about one foot apart. Hold dumbbell in right
hand down at your side. Bend as far as you can to your right.
Return to the starting position. (One repetition.)
Repeat for left side.

10. *Leg Extensions*:
To strengthen the quadriceps.

Equipment: Leg extension machine

Starting Position and Movement:
Sit on the bench of the extension machine. Hold onto the seat
and place feet under the pads of the movable bar. Raise the
weight slowly until your legs are fully extended. Slowly lower
the weight to the starting position. (One repetition.)

11. *Leg Curls*:
To strengthen the hamstrings.

Equipment: Leg curl machine

Starting Position and Movement:
Lie face down on the leg curl machine with your heels placed
under the pads of the movable bar. Raise the lower legs until
they are perpendicular (90 degree angle) to the floor. Slowly
lower the weight to the starting position. (One repetition.)

12. *Squats*:
To strengthen the hamstrings and buttocks.

Equipment: Barbell

Starting Position and Movement:
Stand with feet approximately shoulder width apart, with toes
pointing slightly outward. Place barbell across the shoulders just
below the base of the neck. Position hands so that the bar is
evenly balanced. Lower buttocks into a squat position until
thighs are parallel to the floor. Then rise slowly to the starting
position. (One repetition.)

NOTE: Keep head up and look forward when performing squat. Do not arch back. Always have a spotter for this exercise.

13. *Heel Raise*:

To strengthen the muscles of the calf.

Equipment: Barbell

Starting Position and Movement:
Place barbell across the shoulders just below the base of the neck. Position hands so that the bar is evenly balanced. Then rise on the balls of your feet, bringing your heels off the floor as high as possible. Slowly lower heels to the floor. (One repetition.)
The exercises that have been described in this section are common exercises for the major muscle groups in the body. You may already be familiar with these and other strength training exercises. Additional exercises can be found in books about strength training.

Designing a Program for Muscular Fitness
As you have read, body-weight calisthenics and weight lifting exercises are excellent for developing muscular fitness. Weight training programs are organized by combining exercises into groups of repetitions and sets. *Repetitions* or reps designate the number of times you perform an exercise. A *set* is a series of repetitions. For example, a workout might include two sets of eight repetitions for each lifting exercise. There are many ways to combine repetitions and sets in a weight training program. If you want to concentrate on building strength, you will use heavier weights and do fewer repetitions. For example, you may do three sets of five to eight reps for each exercise. To develop muscular endurance, you will use lighter weights but do more repetitions. Two or three sets of eight to twelve repetitions will build a higher degree of endurance than strength. There are numerous variations of rep and set combinations that have been developed by different weight training experts. Most combinations will give you satisfactory results.
In order to develop strength or endurance, you must work the muscles more than usual. This is the *Principle of Overload*. The

amount of weight you should use for each lift is determined mainly by trial and error. First, you must determine the maximum weight you can lift for each exercise. Weight lifters call this process *maxing out*. Select a suitable starting weight close to but below what you think is the maximum you can lift. If you complete one repetition, add additional weight until you can no longer perform one lift. The last weight at which you can perform one complete lift is your max. Follow this procedure for each lifting exercise. Then, to find your workout weight for each lift, calculate 60% to 80% of the max. The following example will show you how this procedure works.

Your max for the bench press is 175 pounds. Sixty percent of 175 pounds is 105 pounds; 80% is 140 pounds. If you wanted to develop endurance, you would work out at 105 pounds and do more repetitions. To develop strength, use 140 pounds and do fewer repetitions.

You must also apply the Principle of Progression to see continued improvement in muscular fitness. For example, at the beginning of your lifting program you found it hard to bench press 140 pounds for three sets of five reps. In fact, you could complete only three reps in each set. Several weeks later, you could easily complete three sets of five reps. To continue increasing your strength, you should increase your workload and decrease the number of reps. Depending on the exercise, the weight is usually increased by five to ten pounds. As training continues, the workload must be increased progressively if the muscles are to get stronger.

What exercises should you include in a strength training program? In selecting exercises, remember the Principle of Specificity. You must work the muscles that you want to develop. Therefore, exercises should be included for each major muscle group--the shoulders, arms, chest, upper and lower back, abdomen, and legs. For general fitness, a basic program of one or two lifts for each of the major muscle groups is usually sufficient. Athletes may go beyond a basic program. Before adding more specific exercises to your program, analyze the motions that are used in your sports. Determine what muscles are being used. Then select exercises that will strengthen those muscles.

It may be beneficial to perform several different exercises for each muscle group. For example, the shoulder muscles are very complex. If an athlete relies heavily on strong shoulder muscles, different exercises can be used to develop the front, middle, and rear portions of the muscles.

Muscles are designed to work in opposing pairs. As one of the pair contracts, the other relaxes. Movement then takes place. Examples of muscles that work in pairs are the biceps and triceps in the upper arm and the quadriceps and hamstrings in the upper leg. If you work hard to develop only one of the muscles in the pair, you upset the balance between the two. As a result, the muscles are more susceptible to injury. You should always select exercises for each of the opposing muscle groups to achieve balance in strength.

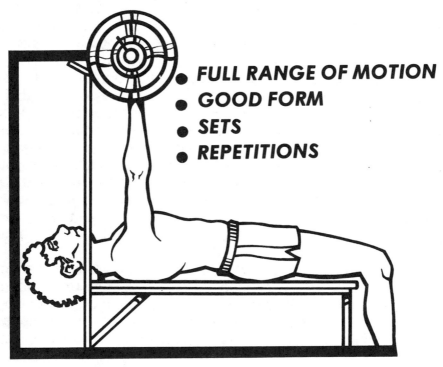

- **FULL RANGE OF MOTION**
- **GOOD FORM**
- **SETS**
- **REPETITIONS**

Illus. 3-2

Training Hints

How can you obtain maximal benefits from your strength training program? The recommendations discussed in this section will help you achieve the results you want.

First, be sure to include flexibility exercises as part of you workout. Stretch out before you begin lifting. Your muscles will work more efficiently after they have been stretched. Stretching will also help prevent muscles strains. Remember to stretch out as part of your "cool-down" to reduce muscular soreness.

Using correct technique when lifting weights is very important. In the past some athletes avoided weight training. They thought they would become "muscle-bound" and lose their flexibility. Recent studies show that, if correct technique is used, flexibility is not lost. Correct technique requires using full range of motion when lifting. Imagine doing a biceps curl through a full range of motion. When raising the weight, the elbows are bent fully so that the bar comes to the chest. When lowering the weight, the elbows are extended completely so that the arms are straight. You have completed the lift with correct technique since you have used full range of motion.

It is also important to use good form when lifting. For best results take approximately two seconds to raise the weight and four seconds to lower the weight. Slowly lowering the weight to the starting position rather than letting it drop will further strengthen the muscles. Poor form involves "cheating" to lift weight that is too heavy. A lazy lifter does not work through a full range of motion but uses momentum to lift a weight. This "lazy" approach produces minimal results. A slight pause between each rep will slow momentum. Arching the back, especially while bench pressing, is another example of poor form. Poor form is often a way of compensating for a weight that is too heavy. As a result, injuries are likely to occur.

Frequency is also important in strength training. For best results, you should follow your workout at least three times a week or every other day. The purpose of alternating workout days is to allow time for the muscles to recover. Strength gains do not take place during the actual workout but during the rest periods between workouts. Daily workouts prevent the muscles from adapting to the workload because of fatigue. If you are a serious lifter, you may want to work out every day. To allow recovery time, try using a split routine training. This routine alternates upper body with lower body training from one day to the next.

Keeping a workout log is a good way for you to check your progress. You can list the lifts in your workout, the weight used for each lift, and the number of reps and sets completed. There are many different forms you can use for a workout log, but the example given below is easy to follow.

In the first column list all of the exercises included in your workout. The second column has room for the date of the workout. This column also contains three small boxes that are diagonally divided in half. In the top half of the box, record the weight you use for that lift. In the bottom half of the box, record the number of reps you complete at that weight. Each box represents a set. If you do two sets, you will complete two boxes. If you do more than three sets, add as many boxes as necessary. By adding additional columns across the page, you can record the workouts for a week on one page.

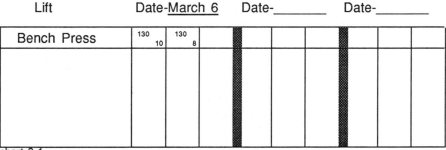

chart 3-1

Personal Muscular Fitness Programs

As you develop a muscular fitness program, you need to answer two questions. Why is the development of muscular fitness important for your daily activities or sports? What is the major goal of your muscular fitness program?

If you are concerned about muscular fitness for good health and appearance, your goals will be different from those of an athlete who is concerned about performance. Workouts for athletes will generally be more strenuous. Also, athletes will usually spend more time weight training. Weight training programs for athletes also differ. Which is more important for an athlete, developing strength or endurance? Note the variations in the sample workout programs that are shown here.

GENERAL FITNESS WORKOUT: 2 sets of 10 reps at 60% of max

Bench Press
Biceps Curl
Triceps Extension
Upright Rowing
Lat Pull-Downs
Side Bends
Sit-Ups
Prone Trunk Lift

40

Leg Extensions
Leg Curls
Side Leg Raise
Heel Raise

STRENGTH WORKOUT: 3 sets of 6 reps at 80% of max

Bench Press
Seated Shoulder Press
Upright Rowing
Shrugs
Biceps Curl
Triceps Extension
Lat Pulldowns
Sit-ups
Squats
Leg Extensions
Leg Curls
Heel Raise

Add additional lifts that develop muscles specific to each sport.

ENDURANCE WORKOUT: 3 sets of 12 reps at 60-70% of max

Seated Press
Upright Rowing
Biceps Curl
Triceps Extension
Lat Pulldowns
Side Bends
Sit-Ups
Squats
Leg Extensions
Leg Curls
Heel Raise

Add additional lifts that develop the muscles specific to each sport.

To develop your own strength training program, turn to Activity
Challenge II in the workbook. Remember to use the ideas that
were discussed in this chapter.

Protein Supplements

One of the most common myths among athletes is that extra protein is necessary to build body size and strength. Look through popular fitness and strength magazines and you will see advertisements for all types of protein supplements. The most popular forms for protein supplements are powders and tablets. Some tablets even come in special "time-release" formulas.

Will eating extra protein or taking protein supplements help you build muscle? For many years it was thought that protein supplements were necessary for athletes. One theory stated that extra protein was needed because the muscles consumed themselves as fuel during exercise. Current research has shown that this theory is incorrect. Very little protein is used as fuel during exercise. When carbohydrates are available, they are used for energy rather than protein. Since the average American diet usually provides more protein than necessary, special supplements are not needed.

How much protein do you need? The Recommended Daily Allowance for teenagers is .41 grams of protein per pound of body weight. The RDA for 15 to 18 year old males is .41 grams of protein per pound of body weight. For females of the same ages, the RDA is .37 grams of protein per pound of body weight[1]. For example, Jack, who is 16 years old, weigh 145 pounds. Based on the RDA, he needs about 59 grams of protein per day (145 pounds x .41 grams = 59.45 grams protein). Fifty-nine grams of protein is equivalent to the protein found in a cheeseburger sandwich, two slices of cheese pizza, and one cup of strawberry yogurt.

Several current research studies show that athletes may need slightly more protein that the average person who is only moderately active. The results of these studies have not been conclusive about the amount of protein needed by athletes, however, the typical American diet provides more than enough protein to meet the needs of most athletes[2]. As a rule, most teenagers consume two to three times the RDA for protein. Probably the only athletes who run the risk of not getting enough dietary protein are those who are on low calorie diets. For a special exercise in estimating your protein intake, turn to Activity Challenge III in your workbook.

Because most diets contain plenty of protein,athletes do not need special protein supplements. Most protein supplements that are sold as aids to athletic performance contain protein mixtures containing casein (milk protein), soy protein, and egg protein. Most of these supplements are extremely expensive. The cost per gram of protein is much more than the price of the ingredients. The protein found in milk, cheese, and yogurt is much less expensive than tablets containing special casein mixtures.

Amino acids supplements are a new type of protein supplement being used by many athletes. Protein is composed of building blocks called amino acids. Twenty different amino acids have been identified. Amino acid supplements contain one amino acid or a combination of two or more amino acids. *Arginine* and *ornithine* are the two most commonly used amino acids. They are theorized to increase the levels of human growth hormone, which could cause growth in muscle tissue. Although many athletes feel that these supplements are beneficial, there is little scientific evidence to support this belief.

Extremely high amounts of protein may be a health risk. High protein intakes may put extra stress on the kidneys. Excess nitrogen from too much protein must be excreted by the kidneys. Excess protein can also cause dehydration, which has a negative effect on athletic performance. The body can dehydrate and overheat because the body fluids are used to excrete the excess nitrogen. Normal body functions can also be upset by amino acid supplements. Large amounts of individual amino acids may interfere with the absorption and use of other amino acids in the body.

Companies that manufacture special supplements are in business to make money. The truth about these products is often stretched. For example, some scientific studies have shown that athletes may need slightly more protein than the RDA. The best and least expensive way to meet this need is to eat more protein foods. However, companies want you to spend money on their products, so they use all types of advertising gimmicks and slogans. Be wary of personal testimonies, unsupported studies, and deceptive advertising in popular sports magazines. When in doubt, save your money. Most authorities on sports nutrition agree that your best source of protein is from the food you eat.

Steroids

Steroid use is a growing problem in the world of athletics. Many athletes who want to increase strength and improve performance take drugs called *anabolic steroids*. Athletes began using anabolic steroids as early as the 1950's. In the 1960's more Olympic and professional athletes began using steroids to improve performance. Today, the use of steroids is increasing among college and high school athletes.

What are anabolic steroids? Anabolic steroids are synthetic versions of the male hormone testosterone. Testosterone is produced naturally by the body and is responsible for the male sex characteristics, such as lowered voice and facial hair. Testosterone also stimulates growth, especially growth of muscle tissue. Taking anabolic steroids increases the level of testosterone in the body. The theory is that larger amounts of testosterone increase the body's ability to build more muscle tissue. Although anabolic steroids increase muscle tissue, the increase in muscle size is temporary. With steroids much of the size increase is the result of fluid build-up in the muscles. When steroid use stops, most of the excess water is lost, causing the muscles to decrease in size.

There are serious risks involved in taking steroids. The body's hormone system has a delicate balance and, when it is upset, there can be some serious consequences. Scientific research is showing that some of the side effects may be reversible when the steroids are discontinued. Other side effects however are permanent.

What are some of the side effects of steroid use? One of the greatest risks to teenaged boys is stunted growth. Many males in their teens are still growing and continue to do so into their early twenties. Anabolic steroids cause premature closure of the growth plates at the ends of the bones. Once these plates close, no further growth in height can take place. If you are tempted to use steroids, ask yourself this question: "Am I willing to stunt my growth?" Other side effects in males include development of acne and loss of hair. When males have too much testosterone in their system, the liver may convert the extra testosterone into estrogen. This shift in hormone balance may result in the development of female-type breast tissue. There can also be a decrease in the size of the testes.

Females who take steroids also experience side effects. The increase in testosterone causes the vocal cords to thicken and results in a deeper voice. The drugs can also increase the growth of facial hair and decrease breast size. In addition, many females experience disrupted menstrual cycles.

Other serious health risks may be experienced by both males and females who take steroids. Liver damage, including the development of liver tumors, has been seen in steroid users.

Steroids can also increase blood cholesterol levels, which can lead to heart disease at an early age.

Besides having physical side effects, steroids can also have psychological side effects - steroids will often cause personality changes by increasing aggressiveness. Bouts of anger and hostility have become known among steroid users as "roid rages." Research is also showing that people who use steroids may develop an addiction to them.

Steroids are classified as "banned" drugs by athletic governing bodies such as the International Olympic Committee, the National Football League, and the National Collegiate Athletic Association. These organizations have instituted drug testing programs to check for steroid use. Penalties range from monetary fines to loss of scholarships, to being dismissed from the team. Some high schools are even considering the use of drug testing as part of routine participation physicals.

Most experts agree that the short-term benefits of steroid use are not worth the risks involved. Many athletes are finding that a high carbohydrate diet and an intensive weight training program will help them gain weight and add strength. This drug-free approach may take longer, but is safer, with longer lasting results. More information on high carbohydrate diets for weight and strength gain will be discussed in Chapter Eight.

Muscular strength and endurance are important for fitness and athletic performance. Hard work and good nutrition will help you develop muscular strength.

CHAPTER SUMMARY--CASE STUDY

Re-read the Case Study that introduced this chapter. Using the information in this chapter, what advice would you give Jon?

1. Why would increased muscular fitness be important for Jon?

2. Explain to Jon the three principles of strength training that he should use in his weight training program?

3. What is the difference in organizing a weight training program to develop muscular strength and a weight training program to develop muscular endurance?

4. How should Jon determine his workload for each exercise in his lifting program?

5. Explain to Jon some of the correct lifting techniques he should use.
   Why is it important to use correct technique?

6. Design a weight training program for Jon. Include the following information:
   -Should Jon use a strength or an endurance workout?
   -How many sets and reps should he do?
   -What percent of his max should he use?
   -List ten lifts that would help Jon develop the muscles he uses in wrestling.

7. What advice would you give Jon about using protein supplements?

8. Tell Jon what you know about steroids.
   Would you recommend that Jon use steroids?
   Explain the reason for your recommendation.

1. Based on information from food and Nutrition Board. Recommended Dietary Allowances, 10th edition, Washington, D.C.: National Academy of Sciences, 1989.

2. Lemon, Peter. Protein and exercise: update 1987. Medicine and Science in Sports and Exercise. Vol. 19 (Supplement), 1987.

4 PUTTING IT TOGETHER: TOTAL CONDITIONING

CASE STUDY

I really want to be ready for tennis this fall. Last season I played second singles and had a 6-9 record. My goal is to improve my win-loss record. Last year I started conditioning two weeks before the team started to practice. I ran one mile three days a week, lifted weights twice a week, and played tennis for one hour every day. How should I train this summer so that I can meet my goal?

--Jennifer, high school senior

Many elements go into the making of a successful athlete-- natural talent, hard work, and the desire for success. The genes you inherit from your parents define the limits of your potential as an athlete, but it is up to you to develop that potential to its greatest degree. The success you achieve depends on your willingness to train and practice in order to make the most of your inherited talents and abilities.

A conditioning program that emphasizes *total* fitness uses all three key areas you have learned about--flexibility, aerobic conditioning, and strength training. A conditioning program that includes these three key areas will help you achieve your full potential as an athlete. Even if you do not participate in organized sports, a general fitness program that includes these three areas will help you stay healthy and fit.

Training Level Requirements

How can you be sure that the training program you design will improve your fitness level? Exercises for developing flexibility, cardiovascular endurance, and muscular strength must be performed at recommended levels for a training effect to take place.

Training to improve fitness has three requirements--*intensity*, *duration*, and *frequency*. Intensity refers to *how hard* you should exercise. Duration means *how long* you should exercise. Frequency indicates *how often* you should exercise. By applying these requirements to each of the three fitness components, you will increase your level of fitness. Let's review what you have learned about these training requirements in the first three chapters.

FLEXIBILITY

INTENSITY: Stretch slowly without bouncing until a slight "tension" is felt in the muscles.

DURATION: Hold the stretched position for 20-30 seconds.

FREQUENCY: Stretch out daily for best results.
A flexibility program can be used by itself or as a "warm-up" and "cool-down" for cardiovascular and strength training sessions.

CARDIOVASCULAR ENDURANCE

INTENSITY: Elevate the pulse rate into the target zone, which is 70-80% of the maximal heart rate.

DURATION: Exercise *continuously* for 20 to 30 minutes.

FREQUENCY: Exercise at least 3 to 4 times per week.

MUSCULAR STRENGTH

INTENSITY: Use 60-80% of the maximum weight you can lift for each exercise. For greatest strength development, use a higher percentage of the "max".

DURATION: For general fitness and toning, do 2 sets of 10 repetitions at 60% of the max for each lift. To

develop muscular endurance, do 3 sets of 12 reps at 60-70% of the max for each lift.
For strength development, do 3 sets of 6 reps at 80% of the max for each lift.

FREQUENCY: Work out at least 3 days per week or every other day.

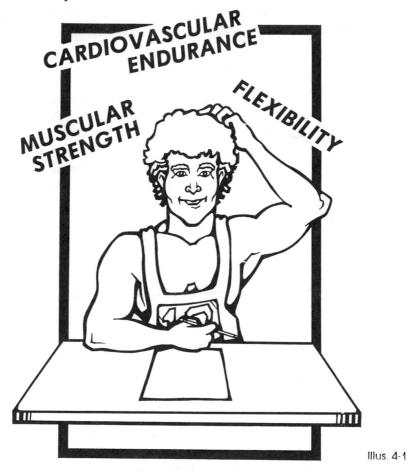

CARDIOVASCULAR ENDURANCE

MUSCULAR STRENGTH

FLEXIBILITY

Illus. 4-1

If you train below these recommended levels, you will see very little improvement in your fitness. Being a "weekend" athlete doesn't do much to develop fitness.

Steps in Planning a Total Conditioning Program

An effective fitness and conditioning program requires planning. A haphazard approach cannot give you the desired results. How should you go about planning an effective conditioning program?

The first step is to determine your present fitness level. The physical requirements related to athletic performance are flexibility, cardiovascular endurance, and muscular strength. These three fitness keys have been discussed in the previous chapters. If you have not had a chance to take the fitness tests you may want to do so at this time.

Once you have determined your present level of fitness for each area, you are ready for step two. You must now ask yourself, "What are my goals?" Is your goal, perhaps, to be a state champion in the hurdles, or is your goal basically to improve your appearance and health? When setting goals, you need to be realistic. Consider the level of fitness you need for your sports or activities. The conditioning program for an athlete should be more difficult than a general fitness program designed for someone who wants to achieve good looks and health.

The third step is to develop a conditioning program that will help you reach your goals. Don't make the mistake of following a carbon-copy of a famous athlete's conditioning program. An elite athlete has had years of conditioning and has developed a program to suit his or her own specific needs. Likewise, you should design your own training program to develop your strengths and correct your weaknesses.

Principles of Conditioning

As you develop your conditioning program, be sure to follow the scientific principles of *Specificity*, *Overload*, and *Progression*. Let's take time to review these principles.

The first principle for program design is the Principle of Specificity. There is very little cross-over in the areas of training. For example, exercises to promote flexibility will not develop cardiovascular fitness or muscular strength. Be sure to include specific activities that develop each fitness area. All too often an athlete concentrates only on one area and neglects the others. Many different conditioning programs can be designed using a variety of exercises. Carefully select the exercises for your conditioning program. The exercises you choose should be ones that will help you meet your fitness goals.

It is also important to use the Principle of Overload in your conditioning program. Increased activity, *overload*, is the basis of physical conditioning. The only way that your body can become stronger is by working harder than normal. By forcing your body to work harder during exercise, you improve your level of fitness.

The Principle of Progression is closely related to the Principle of Overload. To continue improving your fitness level, you must progressively increase the workload used for conditioning activities. This can be done by increasing intensity, duration, or frequency. For example, when it becomes easy for you to jog 20 minutes, you can increase your pace (intensity). The body adapts to a new work overload by becoming stronger. This "adaptation cycle" will usually take from two to four weeks. Once the body can easily handle the workload, there will be no new improvements until the overload is increased again. Training harder to continually improve your fitness level is called the Principle of Progression.

Designing a Total Conditioning Program

Now you are ready to put your training program "on paper." Writing out your program makes it easier to include training requirements and conditioning principles. The following examples will illustrate how to set up a total conditioning program.

Lynne is a high school junior. Her goal is to maintain her weight and achieve good muscle tone. When she designed her conditioning program, she organized her activities as shown below:

FLEXIBILITY

INTENSITY: Static stretching.

DURATION: Hold each stretch for 20 seconds.

FREQUENCY: Stretch before and after each cardiovascular and strength training session.

FLEXIBILITY EXERCISES

Shoulder Stretch
Chest Stretch
Trunk Rotations
Side Stretches

Head to Knees
Leg Curls
Knee to Chest
Seated Hip Stretch
Lunge
Wall Push-Away
Ankle Rotations

CARDIOVASCULAR ENDURANCE

INTENSITY: Target zone--70% of MHR.

DURATION: 30 to 40 minutes.

FREQUENCY: Three times a week.

CARDIOVASCULAR ENDURANCE (AEROBIC) EXERCISES

Aerobic dance class (40 minutes)
Walking (30 minutes)

MUSCULAR STRENGTH

INTENSITY: 60% of max for each lift.

DURATION: Two sets of 10 repetitions.

FREQUENCY: Two days each week.

MUSCULAR STRENGTH EXERCISES

Bench Press
Upright Rowing
Biceps Curl
Triceps Extension
Lat Pulldowns
Side Bends
Leg Extensions
Leg Curls
Heel Raise
Sit-Ups
Prone Trunk Lift

Chris is a sophomore who played on the junior varsity basketball team and wants to play on the varsity team next year. The conditioning program that Chris designed includes these activities:

FLEXIBILITY

INTENSITY: Static stretching.

DURATION: Hold each stretch for 20 seconds.

FREQUENCY: Stretch before and after each cardiovascular and strength training session.

FLEXIBILITY EXERCISES

Arm Rotations
Chest Stretch
Upper Back Stretch
Trunk Rotations
Side Stretches
Head to Knees
Leg Curls
Knee to Chest
Seated Hip Stretch
The Yogi
Wall Push-Away
Ankle Rotations
Ankle Flexions/Extensions

CARDIOVASCULAR ENDURANCE

INTENSITY: Target zone--80% of MHR.

DURATION: 30 minutes.

FREQUENCY: Three times a week.

CARDIOVASCULAR ENDURANCE (AEROBIC) EXERCISES
Jogging

MUSCULAR STRENGTH

INTENSITY: 70% of max for each lift.

DURATION: Three sets of 12 repetitions.

FREQUENCY: Three days each week.

MUSCULAR STRENGTH EXERCISES
Bench Press
Seated Shoulder Press
Upright Rowing
Biceps Curl
Triceps Extension
Wrist Curls
Lat Pulldowns
Side Bends
Leg Extensions
Leg Curls
Heel Raise
Sit-Ups
Prone Trunk Lift

The Activity Challenge in the workbook will help you design your personal total conditioning program. After four to six weeks of training, check your progress in each fitness area. You can do this by retaking the self-evaluation tests and comparing the results with your first test scores. If any changes are needed in your fitness program, make the necessary adjustments at this time.

Training Tips

Once you have put your program "on paper," you are ready to begin training. Workout regularly. By working out at a certain time of the day, training becomes a part of your daily routine. When you are in school, it is often most convenient to workout after school. During the summer, a morning workout may be more practical.

If you have difficulty disciplining yourself to workout, train with a friend. Training is easier when you know that someone else is counting on you. Working out can be fun if you are with other people who have similar interests and goals.

Keeping a daily training diary will also help you stick to your workouts. There are many ways to organize a training diary. If you jog for your aerobic exercise, you can record either the time spent running or the distance you covered. For lifting exercises, you can record the weight, reps, and sets for each lift. You can purchase activity logs in many sporting goods stores or you can design your own log book.

Pre-Season Conditioning

Many high school athletes think that they can "get into shape" quickly at the start of organized team practice. Don't make this mistake! You should think of your sports season as being divided into two phases: pre-season and competitive season.

General conditioning should be emphasized in the pre-season, two to three months *before* the competitive season begins. You should be improving your flexibility, cardiovascular endurance, and strength. The key is to emphasize all fitness areas. You should also concentrate on weak areas. For example, a runner who has a weak upper body can spend time lifting weights to develop more muscular strength. A basketball player who tires easily during the fourth quarter of a game can work on improving cardiovascular endurance.

To help you maintain the specialized skills needed for your sport, you may want to add several game-type activities each week. For example, if you are on the tennis team, playing several games of singles or doubles will be beneficial. Including specialty drills such as shooting baskets or practicing putts can also prepare you for the particular demands of your sports. Improving your skill level is important. However, the activities used to develop specific sport skills do not develop overall fitness. Don't neglect your total conditioning program which is needed to improve your basic fitness level.

If you have faithfully followed your pre-season conditioning program, you will start the competitive season in good physical condition. Instead of having to spend the first two weeks of practice "getting into shape," you will be ready to concentrate on refining your skills and sharpening your performance levels. Pre-season conditioning means competitive success!

There is no easy way to stay physically fit. It takes lots of hard work and dedication. Being healthy and fit for life is a good goal for everyone to have.

CHAPTER SUMMARY--CASE STUDY

Re-read the Case Study that introduced this chapter. Using the information in this chapter, what advice would you give Jennifer?

1. What are three mistakes that Jennifer made in planning her conditioning program last year?

2. What are the three key areas of conditioning that Jennifer should include in her fitness program?

3. Explain the training requirements of intensity, duration, and frequency.
    Discuss how these requirements relate to each of the three key areas of fitness.

4. Explain to Jennifer why a pre-season conditioning program should help her meet her goal of improving her win-loss record.

INTRODUCTION--PART TWO

NUTRITION FOR FITNESS

You've worked on your flexibility, run to develop cardiovascular fitness, and lifted weights to gain strength. Can you add anything else to your training program to improve your fitness level?

The answer is yes--nutritional conditioning, the fourth key to fitness and athletic performance. What you eat does matter. Food is more than just something to keep you from being hungry. Food provides you with the energy and nutrients that your body needs in order to function.

However, there are no magic foods, special food supplements, or secret diets that will turn you into a superstar. Then why worry about your eating habits? Eating *improperly* can keep you from being healthy and performing your best. Even the most dedicated athlete could ruin the chance to excel since a poor diet can affect body size, strength, and stamina.

If you have thought about nutrition, you might have asked yourself several questions: "How can I tell if I'm eating properly?" "What changes do I need to make in my eating habits?" "Will my performance improve if I change my diet?" The following six chapters discuss various aspects of nutritional conditioning. Two chapters explain how foods provide the nutrients and energy you need. Another chapter helps you analyze your eating habits and food selection patterns. Separate chapters discuss topics of special concern to the athlete--weight control, pre-competition meals, and water replacement.

This information and the Activity Challenges in the workbook will help you formulate your own nutritional gameplan which is part of the winning combination.

5 YOU ARE WHAT YOU EAT--- FOOD NUTRIENTS

CASE STUDY

"I'm on the gymnastics team and must watch my weight very carefully. I used to skip meals, but when I got hungry, I frequently snacked on junk food since it was quick and convenient. I never felt as if I had much energy and got tired easily. Last year I missed six weeks of practice and competition because of a stress fracture in my foot. My coach said that I needed to improve my diet, so I'm trying to eat at meal time and select foods that are good for me. In fact, I've started to take a special vitamin supplement that I read about in a sports magazine. The advertisement said that this supplement gives athletes more energy since it is in a time-release formula. What helpful hints can you give me about selecting foods that are good for me?"

--Wendy, high school sophomore

Have you ever wondered what is in the foods you eat--the hamburger sandwich you had for lunch yesterday or the ice cream you ate before going to bed last night? All foods are composed of six different "building blocks" known as nutrients. These nutrients are broken down during digestion into chemical forms that your body can use for energy, for the regulation of various body processes, and for repair of body tissues. The six different nutrient classifications are water, vitamins, minerals, carbohydrates, fat, and protein. Chart 5-1 lists these six nutrient classifications and describes the function of each nutrient.

NUTRIENT CLASSIFICATION TABLE

NUTRIENT	FUNCTION
Water	Regulates body temperature
	Transports nutrients and waste materials
	Component of body fluids
Vitamins	Regulate body processes
Minerals	Regulate body processes
Carbohydrates	Primary energy source
Fats	Concentrated energy source
	Carry fat soluble vitamins and fatty acids
Proteins	Growth and repair of body tissues
	Secondary energy source

Chart 5-1

Water

Water is the most critical nutrient. In fact, a person can survive longer without food than without water. The human body is approximately 60% water. When adequate body water is not available, the body functions less efficiently. Each body cell contains water, which provides the environment for chemical reactions. Water is also used to transport nutrients to the cells and to carry waste products away from them. Another important function of water is to regulate body temperature.

Under normal conditions six to eight glasses of water or other liquids are needed each day to maintain fluid balance. Other liquids that help meet daily fluid requirements are milk, juices, and soups. Foods such as fruits and vegetables also provide liquid since they have a high water content.

For active people, more liquids are necessary to replace water lost through perspiration. In fact, water is so important for active people and athletes that Chapter 10 discusses water in greater detail.

Vitamins

Vitamins regulate all chemical reactions in the body. They are used in important processes such as growth and release of energy. Scientists have currently discovered 13 vitamins. Each vitamin was given a letter name in order of its discovery. A chemical or scientific name can also be used to identify a vitamin. For example, Vitamin C may be identified as ascorbic acid.

Only small amounts of vitamins are needed. Since they cannot be manufactured by your body, they must come from the foods you eat. Foods may contain both natural and synthetic vitamins. Natural vitamins occur naturally in food. Synthetic vitamins are produced in a laboratory and are then added to food products. Foods that have synthetic vitamins added to them will be labeled *enriched* or *fortified*.

Vitamins have been divided into two categories. The *water-soluble* vitamins are Vitamin B Complex, which is composed of eight different vitamins, and Vitamin C. These nine vitamins will dissolve in water. You need to replace water-soluble vitamins daily since your body stores them only in very small amounts, In fact, when the body receives an excess of these vitamins, they are excreted in the urine.

The *fat-soluble* vitamins are Vitamins A, D, E, and K. The fat-soluble vitamins dissolve in fat rather than in water. Any excess of these vitamins are stored in the liver and in the fatty tissues of the body. Taking too many fat-soluble vitamins can be dangerous since they can build to toxic or poisonous levels.

Each vitamin has certain functions to perform, and all vitamins are found in a wide variety of foods. Let's take a look at the vitamins that are especially important for active people.

THIAMINE (VITAMIN B_1)

Thiamine is needed to release energy from carbohydrates. When energy requirements are high, such as during exercise or athletic activity, there is a greater need for thiamine. Since you consume more food when you are active, the amount of thiamine in your diet is automatically increased.

Pork is the richest food source of thiamine. Other good sources are enriched or whole grain products, nuts, and milk products.

RIBOFLAVIN (VITAMIN B_2)

Riboflavin helps cells use oxygen for the release of energy from food.

Meats are good sources of riboflavin as are milk products. Enriched or whole grain products also supply riboflavin.

NIACIN

Niacin is also used to help release energy from carbohydrates.

Foods rich in niacin include meats, peanut butter and nuts, and enriched or whole grain products.

VITAMINS B$_6$ and B$_{12}$

Vitamins B$_6$ and B$_{12}$ are used in the development of red blood cells, which carry oxygen throughout the body.
Oxygen is needed to release energy from the foods you eat.
Good sources of these vitamins are meat, poultry, and fish.

FOLIC ACID, PANTOTHENIC ACID, and BIOTIN

Folic acid, pantothenic acid, and biotin are other less familiar members of the Vitamin B Complex. Like the other B vitamins, these three vitamins also have various roles in metabolizing nutrients for energy. Folic acid is also important in the development of red blood cells.

Dark green leafy vegetables are good sources of folic acid. Pantothenic acid and biotin are found in whole grain products.

VITAMIN C

Vitamin C is important for healing wounds and also for strengthening the walls of the blood vessels. Vitamin C also helps increase the body's resistance to infections.

Good sources of Vitamin C include citrus fruits, strawberries, potatoes, tomatoes, broccoli, and cabbage.

VITAMIN A

Vitamin A helps your body resist infections by keeping the skin and mucous membrane healthy. In addition, Vitamin A is important for maintaining good vision in dim light.

Good sources of Vitamin A include dark yellow and green leafy vegetables and fortified milk products.

VITAMIN D

Vitamin D is often called the "Sunshine Vitamin" because it can by made from the action of sunlight on the skin. Vitamin D is needed for the formation of teeth and bones. If Vitamin D is not present, calcium will not crystalize in the bones. As a result, the bones will not grow properly and will be weak.

The best food sources of Vitamin D are fortified dairy products and fish liver oils.

VITAMIN E

The main role of Vitamin E is that of an *antioxidant*. This means that Vitamin E protects Vitamin A, Vitamin C, and unsaturated fatty acids from being destroyed in your body by oxygen.

Vitamin E is found in vegetable oils, margarine, and green leafy vegetables. Whole grain products, including wheat germ, are also good sources of Vitamin E.

VITAMIN K

Vitamin K is an essential factor in the clotting of blood. If enough Vitamin K is not present, bleeding will continue longer before a clot can form to stop the bleeding.

The best food sources to provide Vitamin K are green leafy vegetables.

Chart 5-2 provides a quick reference about the classification of vitamins, their functions, and food sources.

Water-Soluble Vitamins:	Funtions:	Food Sources:
Vitamin B Complex Thiamine (B$_1$)	Used in release of energy from carbohydrates Promotes functioning of nervous system	Meat, especially pork; enriched or whole grain products; milk products
Riboflavin (B$_2$)	Assists cells in using oxygen to release energy Promotes healthy skin	Meats; enriched or whole grain products; milk products
Niacin	Used in release of energy from carbohydrate Used in formation of fatty acids for energy	Meats; peanut butter; enriched or whole grain products
Vitamins B$_6$ and B$_{12}$	Used in development of red blood cells	Meats; poultry; fish
Folic Acid	Helps metabolize nutrients for energy Used in development of red blood cells	Dark green leafy vegetables

Pantothenic Acid and Biotin	Helps metabolize nutrients for energy	Whole grain products
Vitamin C	Assists in healing of wounds Increases resistance to infections Strengthens blood vessels	Citrus fruits; strawberries; potatoes; tomatoes;cabbage; broccoli
Fat-Soluble Vitamins:	Functions:	Food Sources:
Vitamin A	Increases resistance to infections Promotes health of eyes and skin	Carrots; other deep yellow vegetables; fortified milk and margarine
Vitamin D "Sunshine" Vitamin	Aids in absorption of calcium for development of bones and teeth	Fortified dairy products; can be manufactured in the body by action of sunlight on the skin
Vitamin E	Prevents vitamins and fatty acids from being destroyed	Vegetable oils; margarine; butter; wheat germ; green leafy vegetables'
Vitamin K	Used for blood clotting	Green leafy vegetables

chart 5-2

Minerals

Minerals are another of the major food nutrient categories. Like vitamins, they are important for building and regulating body processes. Three of these minerals, calcium, phosphorus, magnesium, are needed in relatively large amounts. Sodium, chloride, and potassium are other major minerals. These three minerals are often called *electrolyte* minerals. Other minerals such as iodine, zinc, and iron are known as "trace" minerals, since they are needed only in small amounts.

Recommended Daily Dietary Allowances have been established for calcium, phosphorus, magnesium, iodine, zinc, and iron. A well-balanced diet should provide you with all the necessary minerals your body needs. You should know more about the importance of these minerals.

CALCIUM

Calcium is present in the body in greater amounts than any other mineral. It performs many important functions in the body. The main use of calcium is in the formation of teeth and bones. Calcium also plays a major role in regulating nerve and muscle activity and in maintaining a regular heart beat.

Dairy products are the best sources of calcium. Green leafy vegetables also contain useful amounts of calcium.

PHOSPHORUS

Phosphorus also plays an important role in the development of teeth and bones. Phosphorus must be present for your body to be able to absorb and use calcium. It is recommended that phosphorus and calcium should be available in a 1:1 ratio.

Milk is the best source of phosphorus since it is found in a 1:1 ratio with calcium. Other dairy products, meats, and eggs are also good sources of phosphorus.

Teenagers should be aware that drinking too many carbonated beverages can interfere with the balance of calcium and phosphorus. Carbonated beverages, which are high in phosphorus, can upset the 1:1 calcium-phosphorus ratio. When carbonated beverages replace milk or are consumed in large amounts, less calcium than phosphorus is provided in the diet. The calcium that is included becomes less available for absorption and use in bone development.

MAGNESIUM

In addition to helping deposit calcium in teeth and bones, magnesium is involved in helping the cells produce energy.

Foods high in magnesium include meats, dried beans and peas, and whole grain products.

SODIUM-CHLORINE-POTASSIUM

These three major minerals are known as *electrolyte* minerals. These minerals are called electrolytes because they carry an electrical charge. Electrolytes have an important role in regulating water balance in the body.

Sodium and potassium are especially important in the transmission of nerve impulses and for muscle contraction.

Electrolyte minerals are available in a wide variety of foods. Table salt (sodium chloride) is the most common source of sodium and chlorine. Other foods high in sodium include canned soups and snack foods such as crackers, chips, and pretzels. Good sources of potassium include citrus fruits, bananas, potatoes, and tomatoes.

IODINE

Iodine is a part of the hormones produced by the thyroid gland. These hormones help regulate growth and the body's metabolic rate.

Good sources of iodine include *iodized* salt, fish, and other seafoods.

ZINC

Zinc has several important functions in the body. It is involved in digestion and the release of energy from foods. It is also necessary for proper cell growth and repair.

Good sources of zinc include meats, poultry, and whole grain products.

IRON

Even though iron is needed in only very small amounts, it is critical for energy production. Iron forms a part of *hemoglobin*, which is found in the red blood cells. Hemoglobin is responsible for transporting oxygen to the cells. If iron levels are low, you are likely to feel weak and become fatigued easily. This is because your cells are not receiving the oxygen they need to produce energy. Low iron intake can cause an iron deficiency called *anemia*. Iron-deficiency anemia can be detected by measuring the hemoglobin level in the blood.

There are two forms of dietary iron. Iron that is found in meats is most easily absorbed. This type of iron is called *heme* iron. Red meats such as beef and pork contain more iron than poultry and fish. Iron from plant sources are absorbed less efficiently than iron from meats. Dried fruits, green leafy vegetables, and enriched grain products are fairly good plant sources of iron. Vitamin C improves iron absorption. Therefore, try to eat a good source of vitamin C along with foods that contain iron.

Chart 5-3 provides a quick reference about the functions and food sources of minerals.

Major Minerals:	Functions:	Food Sources:
Calcium	Used to form bones and teeth Used to regulate muscle contraction	Dairy products; green leafy vegetables
Phosphorus	Combines with calcium for strengthening bones and teeth	Dairy products; meat; poultry; fish; eggs; whole grain foods
Magnesium	Aids cells in energy production	Meats; dried beans,peas; whole grain foods
Sodium	Used in maintaining water balance Helps transmit nerve impulses for muscle contraction	Table salt; salted snack foods; canned soup
Chlorine	Used in maintaining water balance	Table salt
Potassium	Used in maintaining water balance Helps transmit nerve impulses for uscle contraction	Citrus fruits; bananas; potatoes;tomatoes
Trace Minerals:	Functions:	Food Sources:
Iodine	Helps in regulating growth and metabolic rate	Iodized salt; fish; shellfish
Zinc	Needed for cell growth and repair	Meats; whole grain products
Iron	Used to form meats; hemoglobin in the red blood cells	Liver;, green leafy vegetables; raisins; dates; dried apricots

Chart 5-3

Vitamin and Mineral Supplements

How can you tell if you are getting proper amounts of vitamins and minerals? The National Academy of Sciences has published a set of guidelines known as Recommended Daily Dietary Allowances, which outlines the nutrient levels needed by the average healthy person. A safety margin over and above minimum amounts is built into these recommendations, making allowances for people, such as athletes, who may have higher nutrient demands.

Scientific studies conclude that vitamins and minerals taken in excess of the normal RDA's do not enhance athletic performance. If you eat three meals a day and include a wide variety of foods, vitamin and mineral supplements are an unnecessary expense. Don't depend on supplements to make up for a poor diet. However, if you are constantly skipping meals and eating lots of "junk" food, a "one-a-day" type vitamin that contains 100% of the RDA may be beneficial. Avoid megadoses (amounts 10 times greater than the RDA) of vitamins and minerals unless they have been prescribed by your doctor. Excess amounts of fat-soluble vitamins are stored in the body and can build to toxic levels. In extreme case of overdose, death can result. Most megadoses of water-soluble vitamins do not pose a health risk because they are excreted in the urine. However, large amounts of some vitamins may cause problems in susceptible individuals. For example, too much Vitamin B_6 can cause nerve disorders. Another problem with megadoses of water-soluble vitamins is that your body may come to rely on these large amounts. When you reduce the vitamin to the RDA level, your body may develop signs of a vitamin deficiency.

Special formula vitamin and mineral supplements that are advertised for athletes in sports magazines will not improve athletic performance. Although deficiencies of certain vitamins and minerals may impair performances, there is no evidence that "more is better." Think of vitamins and minerals as a football team, with each one having its own position. You don't need more than one quarterback. If you do, the team doesn't work together properly! Too much of one vitamin or mineral can affect the teamwork of the other vitamins and minerals. Activity Challenge I in the workbook will help you learn more about advertising claims for vitamin and mineral supplements. Remember that pills cannot replace a well-balanced diet.

Special Dietary Concerns for Females

Current research studies show that female athletes often run the risk of anemia and stress fractures. These problems are related to iron and calcium deficiencies. Many female distance runners, gymnasts, and dancers want to maintain a low body weight because they think it will help improve performance. To keep their weight low, they eat less than they should. Many of the foods eliminated from their diets are foods that are high in iron and calcium. As a result females are more likely to develop anemia and stress fractures.

Female athletes may want to consider taking a multiple vitamin supplement that contains iron to prevent iron-deficiency anemia. Females tend to be more deficient in iron than males because of lower caloric intake and blood losses during menstruation. Iron is necessary for forming hemoglobin in the red blood cells. These cells transport oxygen from the lungs to the muscles, where energy is released. When the muscles do not receive enough oxygen, they tire more quickly and performance deteriorates. Foods such as liver, red meats, turkey, dried apricots, dates, and raisins are high in iron. Enriched grain products are also sources of iron. Foods containing Vitamin C aid in the absorption of iron while others containing caffeine and tannic acid (tea) interfere with iron absorption. Therefore, when you eat a bowl of iron-enriched cereal or take an iron supplement, a glass of orange juice helps your body absorb more of the iron. Avoid megadoses of iron--they can be dangerous.

When females athletes eliminate dairy products from their diet to maintain a low body weight, stress fractures often occur. Low calcium intake may be one of the causes of stress fractures. Another problem related to stress fractures is *amenorrhea*, which is lack of menstrual periods. Weakness in the bones because of decreased bone density has been discovered in female athletes who develop amenorrhea. Amenorrhea results in lower levels of the female hormone estrogen, which is needed for calcium absorption. Low calcium intake and decreased estrogen levels cause the bones to become weak. Weak bones are more susceptible to stress fractures than are strong bones. Females with amenorrhea should see their doctor. Calcium supplements and estrogen replacement therapy may be recommended to treat amenorrhea. Avoid taking calcium supplements on your own. Too much calcium can contribute to the development of kidney stones and irregular heart beat. Problems with low calcium intake and amenorrhea could lead to *osteoporosis* later in life. Osteoporosis is a calcium deficiency disease that results in brittle and weak bones. Adequate calcium intake is a special concern for women of all ages.

Carbohydrates

Carbohydrates are the body's main energy source since they are quickly digested and absorbed. Nutrients that provide energy contain Calories. Carbohydrates contains four Calories per gram. The three types of carbohydrates found in foods are sugars, starches, and fiber.

Sugars are the simplest type of carbohydrate. Fructose is the sugar found naturally in fruits; lactose is the sugar naturally occurring in milk. Table sugar is known as sucrose. During digestion, these sugars are broken down into *glucose*, which the body uses for energy. Fruits contain a high percentage of natural sugars. Syrups and jelly are almost all refined sugar, as are candies and soft drinks.

Starches compose the second group of carbohydrates. These complex forms of carbohydrate are also broken down into glucose during digestion. Foods such as breads, cereals, rice, pastas, and potatoes are examples that contain a high percentage of starch.

As you have read, both sugars and starches are converted into glucose during digestion. It is then used as an energy source by the central nervous system and the muscles. If glucose is not needed immediately for energy, small amounts can be stored in the liver and muscles. This storage form of carbohydrate is called *glycogen*. During the first few minutes of physical activity, glucose is the primary energy source. However, the body then begins to use glycogen, which is converted back into glucose, as the main fuel source. When glycogen stores are used or depleted, an athlete becomes exhausted. Lack of carbohydrate causes feelings of weakness, hunger, dizziness, and nausea. Therefore, glucose and glycogen are critical for athletic performance. Chart 5-4 shows how the body uses sugars and starches for energy.

CARBOHYDRATES

Sugars   Starches

Digested into simple sugar known as *glucose*.

Used for immediate energy by the central nervous system and the muscles.

Extra amounts are stored in the liver and muscles as *glycogen*. It can be re-converted into *glucose* when needed for energy.

Chart 5-4

The last type of carbohydrate is cellulose, commonly known as fiber or roughage. Although humans cannot digest fiber, it has the important function of preventing constipation by giving bulk to the material moving through the digestive tract. High fiber foods include whole grain products, bran, seeds, nuts, and raw fruits and vegetables.

Fats

Another of the body's fuel sources is fat. Fat is the most concentrated energy source, supplying nine Calories per gram. This is more than twice the energy that carbohydrate provides. However, fat is used less efficiently, since it requires more oxygen to burn. It usually takes 20 to 30 minutes of exercise before enough fat can be metabolized for energy.

Triglycerides are the most common form of fat found in foods. During digestion, triglycerides are broken down into one molecule of glycerol and three units of fatty acids. These *free fatty acids* then become the primary source of energy.

Free fatty acids are grouped into two categories depending upon their chemical structure. The two categories of fat are *saturated fatty acids* and *unsaturated fatty acids*. *Saturated fatty acids* are solid at room temperature and generally come from animal sources. Meats, poultry, dairy products, and egg yolks contain saturated fat. Exceptions are palm and palm kernel oil and coconut oil, which are highly saturated. These oils are commonly used in whipped toppings and other processed foods. *Unsaturated fatty acids* are liquid at room temperature and come from vegetable sources. Examples are corn oil, sunflower oil, and soybean oil. Chart 5-5 shows how fats are classified.

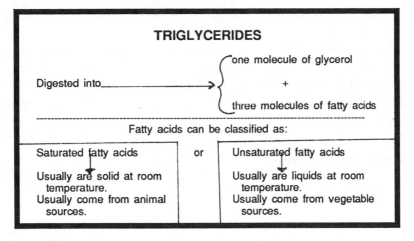

TRIGLYCERIDES

Digested into ⎯⎯⎯⎯⎯⎯⎯⎯⎯⎯⎯⎯⎯⟶ {
one molecule of glycerol

+

three molecules of fatty acids

Fatty acids can be classified as:

Saturated fatty acids	or	Unsaturated fatty acids
Usually are solid at room temperature. Usually come from animal sources.		Usually are liquids at room temperature. Usually come from vegetable sources.

Chart 5-5

Protein

Although protein contains four calories per gram and can provide energy, it is used as an energy source only as a last resort. The primary purposes of protein are for growth and repair of tissues and for regulation of body processes.

Protein molecules are composed of building blocks known as *amino acids*. During digestion the protein you eat is broken down into its amino acids, which are absorbed into the blood stream. Your body can then reassemble the amino acids into new protein forms that each type of cell needs for building, repair, or growth. If there is not enough carbohydrate in the diet, protein can be used for energy. Using protein for energy is undesirable. When protein is used for energy, there usually is not enough protein for growth and repair of body tissues.

Your body needs 22 different amino acids. Nine of these amino acids are called *essential*, because your body cannot manufacture them. Essential amino acids come only from the foods you eat. The remaining 13 amino acids are called *non-essential amino acids*. This does not mean that they are unimportant. It means that it is possible for the body to make these amino acids.

Foods that contain protein are classified as *complete* or *incomplete* protein. A food that contains all nine essential amino acids is called a *complete protein*. Generally foods from animal sources contain complete protein. Examples are meats, poultry, fish, eggs, and dairy products. Soybeans and soy products, such as tofu, are the exceptions since they contain all essential amino acids.

A food which lacks one or more of the nine essential amino acids is called an *incomplete protein*. Foods from plant sources contain incomplete protein. Examples of incomplete protein foods are nuts, dried beans, cereals, and bread products. When an incomplete protein food is eaten with another food containing the missing amino acid, the combination then provides complete protein. A good example of combining two incomplete protein foods to provide complete protein is a peanut butter sandwich made with whole grain bread. Chart 5-6 will help you review the composition of protein.

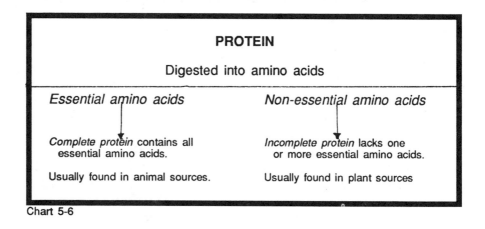

Chart 5-6

For a review of food nutrients, turn to Activity Challenge II in the workbook.

U.S. Recommended Daily Dietary Allowances

Earlier in this chapter you read about Recommended Daily Dietary Allowances (RDAs). RDAs have been established for protein, ten vitamins, and six minerals. Safe and adequate intakes for an additional three vitamins and nine minerals have also been identified. These recommendations can be used as guidelines for determining your nutrient requirements. However, these recommendations do not mean that these intake levels have to be met *exactly* every day. As long as the RDAs are met over the period of time, nutrient deficiencies should not occur.

Nutrition Labeling

Learning to use nutrition labeling is a good way to help you choose foods that will meet your nutrition requirements. Almost one-half of the food packaged in the United States carries nutritional labeling. Nutrition labeling is required by law for food products that are enriched or fortified. Products that make a nutritional claim must also be labeled. Foods which are not in either of these categories may be labeled even though it is not required.

The information that must be included in nutrition labeling is regulated by the Food and Drug Administration (FDA). A nutrition label has two sections. The first part gives the number of Calories and the grams of protein, carbohydrate, and fat in a given serving size. The number of servings is also given. The second part of the label shows the amounts of protein and at least seven vitamins and minerals as *percentages* of the RDA.

What does the label on a jar of peanut butter tell you about its nutritional value? Take a few minutes to study this information.

PEANUT BUTTER

Nutrition Information Per Serving

Serving Size	2 Tablespoons
Servings Per Container	16

Calories 190
Protein . . . . 8 g
Carbohydrate . . . . 3 g
Fat . . . . 16 g

Percentage of U.S. RDA

Protein	 15	Riboflavin	 2
Vitamin A	 0	Niacin	 20
Vitamin C	 0	Calcium	 0

How many Calories come from the peanut butter in a peanut butter and jelly sandwich? According to the label, if you make the sandwich with two tablespoons of peanut butter, you will consume approximately 190 Calories. Most of the Calories are from fat, since a serving contains 16 grams of fat compared to 8 grams of protein and 3 grams of carbohydrate. According to the nutrient percentage chart, a serving of peanut butter supplies 15% of your daily protein requirement, but contains no Vitamin A or Vitamin C. However, it contributes 20% or $\frac{1}{5}$ of your daily niacin requirement. Turn to Activity Challenge III in the workbook for more practice on reading nutrition labels.

The Food Guide Pyramid

What is the easiest way to determine if you are getting the nutrients you need? Learning about the Food Guide Pyramid will help you become an "expert" on nutrition easily and quickly.

Foods are classified into food groups according to the major nutrients they contain. By eating the recommended number of servings from each group every day, you'll be selecting from a variety of foods that will provide the nutrients to keep you healthy and fit. Let's take a closer look at the Food Guide Pyramid, shown in Illustration 5-1.

Food Guide Pyramid
A Guide to Daily Food Choices

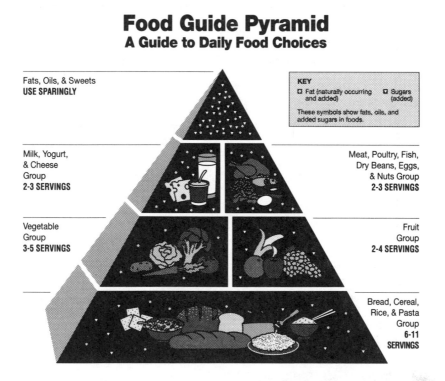

illus 5-1   Source: U.S. Department of Agriculture/U.S. Department of Health and Human Services.

The *Bread, Ceral, Rice, and Pasta Group* is composed of foods made from grains. Foods in this group are high in complex carbohydrates. Enriched and fortified grain products are good sources of B complex vitamins and iron. A wide variety of foods fit into this category. It is recommended that you eat six to eleven servings from the Bread Group each day.

Cerals--hot or cold
Breads--enriched white, whole
    wheat, rye
Rolls--muffins, biscuits
Pastas--macaroni, spaghetti,
    noodles

Rice
Grits
Pancakes, Waffles
Crackers--saltine, graham
Tortillas

The next two groups in the Food Pyramid are the *Vegetable Group* and the *Fruit Group.* Eating a wide variety of vegetables and fruits is important. Vegetables and fruits are high in Vitamins A and C. They are also good sources of fiber. It is recommended that you include at least three to five servings from the Vegetable Group and two to four servings from the Fruit Group each day.

High Vitamin C vegetables--potatoes, green pepper cauliflower,
                cabbage
High Vitamin A vegetables--spinach, kale, broccoli carrots, sweet
                potatoes, pumpkin, winter squash
High Vitamin A fruits--cantaloupe, peaches, apricots

The *Milk, Yogurt,* and *Cheese Group* is composed of foods that are good sources of calcium, riboflavin, and protein. The number of recommended servings from the Milk Group is based on age. Teenagers and young adults need three servings per day. Adults should have two servings daily.

Milk--whole milk, low-fat milk, skim milk, buttermilk, chocolate milk
Cheese
Yogurt and frozen yogurt
Custard and pudding
Ice Cream and ice milk

The *Meat, Poultry, Fish, Dry Beans, Eggs,* and *Nuts Group* is composed of foods that are good sources of protein. Many of the foods from this group are also good sources of iron. A wide variety of foods are found in this group. Two to three servings from the Meat Group are recommended each day.

Red meats--beef, pork, veal, lamb
Poultry--chicken, turkey, duck
Fish and shellfish
Eggs
Dried beans and peas--navy beans, kidney beans, pinto beans,
        soybeans, split peas
Eggs
Nuts and peanut butter
Tofu

The *Fats, Oils, and Sweet Group* is composed of foods that are high in fat, high in sugar, or are high in both fat and sugar. The foods in this groups are high in Calories and have little or no nutritional value. Foods from this group should be used sparingly.

High fat foods--butter, margarine, salad dressings,
        mayonnaise, whipping cream, sour cream,
        bacon, potato chips
High sugar foods--jelly, jam, syrups, candy, soft drinks
High fat and sugar foods--pies, cakes, cookies, pastries,
        doughnuts

The small triangles and circles shown in the Food Pyramid represent fats and sugars. The triangles represent fat that occurs naturally in food or fat that has been added. The small circles represent sugar added to foods. Most of these symbols are found in the Fats and Sweets Group. Notice that foods in the other food groups can also contain fat and sugar but the amounts are much smaller. For example, cheese from the Milk Group contains fat and canned fruits from the Fruit Group may contain added sugar.

It's easy to build your diet using the Food Pyramid. When you look at the Food Pyramid you will see that foods from the Bread Group and foods from the Vegetable and the Fruit Groups should be eaten in the largest amounts. Just as they form the base of the pyramid, so should they form the base of your diet. You then continue to build your diet by adding foods from the Milk Group and from the Meat Group. Remember that foods from one group don't replace foods from another group. All of them are important for good health.

How many serving should you eat each day from the five main food groups? Be sure to eat <u>at least</u> the lowest number of recommended servings for each group. However, teenaged girls and boys should aim for the number of servings recommended in Chart 5-7 to meet their daily Calorie requirements.

Teen Girls	Food Group	Teen Boys
9	Bread	11
4	Vegetable	5
3	Fruit	4
3	Milk	3
2	Meat	3

Chart 5-7

The "Food Find" puzzle in Activity Challenge IV in the Workbook will give you practice in classifying foods according to the Food Guide Pyramid.

Using the Food Guide Pyramid

As you become familiar with classifying foods according to the food groups, checking nutrient intake becomes very quick and easy. First, record everything you eat or drink in a day. Also list the number of servings and estimate serving sizes. Then put the foods you listed into their proper food groups. Next, count the number of servings you had for each food. For example, if you had ½ cup of milk on your cereal at breakfast, it would be counted as ½ serving from the Milk Group. When everything is categorized, add fractions of servings and whole servings to get the total number of servings for each food group. You can then compare the number of servings that you had with the number that are recommended. Remember that the serving recommendations are minimum amounts. It is very likely that you may have more servings than the number that are recommended. Activity Challenge V in the workbook will show you how to give your diet a check-up for nutrient intake. By meeting the requirements of the Food Group Pyramid, you will supply your body with the nutrients necessary for fitness and athletic performance.

CHAPTER SUMMARY--CASE STUDY

Re-read the Case Study that introduced this chapter. Using the information in this chapter, what advice would you give to Wendy?

1. What are the six different types of nutrients that Wendy needs for good health and fitness?

2. Why should Wendy try to select foods that are high in iron? Name four foods that are good sources of iron.

3. What might have been a cause of Wendy's stress fracture? What should she do to help prevent future problems with stress fractures?

4. What recommendations would you give Wendy about taking a vitamin and mineral supplement?

5. Why should Wendy try to include foods in her diet that are high in carbohydrates?
    Name five foods that are good carbohydrate sources.

6. Why should Wendy learn to read nutrition labels on food packages?

7. Explain to Wendy how she should use the Food Guide Pyramid to plan her meals.

8. Why does Wendy need to limit the number of servings she has from the Fats and Sweets Group?

6 CALORIES--FOOD AS FUEL

CASE STUDY

I like to run, bike, and swim during the summer, so I decided to enter a triathlon in August. To train for this event, I've been swimming and biking three times a week and running four times. That adds up to ten training sessions each week, so I'm doing double workouts on some days. I'm eating more than I normally do, but I know that I'm using lots of energy with the extra training. I wonder how much I need to eat so that I have enough energy to train. Are there any foods that are better than others to keep my energy levels high?

--Mike, college freshman

Active people work and play hard. The more active you are, the more energy you need. Even at rest, your body is constantly using energy for maintaining basic functions. During physical activity and exercise, extra energy is needed for the muscles to work. Where do you get the energy for a one hour fitness walk? Where do you get the energy you need to swim the 100 meter backstroke in a school record time? Your energy comes from the food you eat.

Calories--Food Energy

The unit used in measuring body energy is the Calorie. You should understand that Calories are not "things" in foods; foods do not contain Calories as they contain nutrients. Then what is a

Calorie? *A calorie is a unit used to measure heat energy.* There are two types of calories. A calorie (written with a small c) is defined *as the amount of heat necessary to raise one gram of water one degree Celsius.* A Calorie (written with a capital C) or kilocalorie is 1000 times larger than a small calorie. The energy values of foods and physical activities are measured in the *kilocalorie*, which is defined as the *amount of heat needed to raise one kilogram of water (one liter) one degree Celsius.* In nutrition the energy values of food and activity are most commonly written as Calories, spelled with a capital C rather than with a small c.

When food is metabolized in the body, it releases heat that is measured in Calories (kilocalories). The number of Calories in any given food may be determined by burning it in a special container called a bomb calorimeter. When the food is burned, all the heat that is produced warms a known amount of water in the container by a precisely measured amount. The amount of heat energy released is measured in Calories which expresses the amount of energy your body receives from that food.

The number of Calories foods supply depend upon their nutrient composition. You'll remember than three nutrients provide Calories:

Carbohydrates	4 Calories per gram
Proteins	4 Calories per gram
Fats	9 Calories per gram

The other three nutrients--vitamins, minerals, and water--contain no Calories. Therefore, they do not provide energy. Instead, they are used to regulate various body processes. Foods are seldom all carbohydrate, protein, or fat, but are generally a mixture of two or three of the energy nutrients plus various vitamins and minerals. Water content also varies from one food to another.

In your science classes you may have learned that energy is neither created nor destroyed; it is only changed from one form to another. This change happens to the food you eat. During digestion, the energy nutrients are *broken down* through various chemical reactions into forms that your body can use. Carbohydrates are converted into glucose, fats into fatty acids, and proteins into amino acids. Glucose and fatty acids, the main fuel sources, are transported by the blood to the muscle cells where they combine with oxygen. The result is the production of energy and carbon dioxide. This process is called oxidation, since oxygen is needed to release the energy from food. This equation summarizes the oxidation process:

Glucose

+ Oxygen ⟶ Energy + Carbon dioxide

Fatty acids

Once this reaction takes place in the muscle cells, energy is available for the body to use for its activities.

Calories for Basal Metabolism

How many Calories do you need? How much food do you need to eat to meet your energy requirement? Your total energy need is determined by two factors:

1. The number of Calories necessary to maintain the body at rest. (Basal Metabolic Rate)
2. The number of Calories needed for physical activity.

The caloric requirement to maintain the body at complete rest is the basal metabolic rate or BMR. Even at complete rest the body needs energy for basic functions such as pumping blood, breathing, and maintaining body temperature. Energy is also necessary for brain function and growth and repair of body cells. Basal metabolic rate is influenced by several factors. Body size is one of these factors. Larger individuals generally have higher metabolic rates than those who are smaller. A person's sex affects BMR. Males usually have higher basal metabolic rates than females of the same height and age. Because men have more muscle, they have a lower percentage of body fat than females. Lean muscle tissue burns more Calories than fat and raises the BMR. Physically fit individuals, whether male or female, burn more Calories than people who are less active and have a higher percentage of body fat. Younger persons also have higher metabolic rates. The BMR decreases with age, especially after growth is complete.

Your basal metabolic rate can be determined in a laboratory through a complex testing procedure. However, you can estimate the number of Calories needed for your basal metabolism by using the following method.

MALES:

Weight in pounds   x   11   =   Calories to meet BMR

_____   x   11   =   _____

FEMALES:

Weight in pounds   x   11   =   Calories to meet BMR (unadjusted)

_____   x   11   =   _____

Unadjusted Calories for BMR   x   .90   =   Adjusted Calories to meet BMR

_____   x   .90   =   _____

*The adjusted Calories to meet the BMR takes into account the lower metabolic rate of women.

To show you how these formulas work, we'll use Jim and Shelley as examples. Jim, who weighs 165 pounds, needs approximately 1815 Calories to meet the needs of his BMR. (165 pounds x 11 = 1815). Shelley, who weighs 120 pounds, requires only about 1188 Calories for her metabolic rate. (120 pounds x 11 = 1320. Unadjusted Calories 1320 x .90 = 1188 Adjusted Calories.) Females should note the additional step that adjusts for sex differences in the BMR. By applying the same procedures, you should be able to estimate the number of Calories you need to meet basal metabolic requirements.

Calories for Physical Activity

The second factor influencing your caloric needs is level of physical activity. Everyone uses Calories above those needed to maintain the body at rest. The muscles need energy to maintain posture and move the body. While some people spend most of their time sitting or standing, others are extremely active. The amount of energy needed for physical activity depends on the number and size of the muscles you use and how long, how hard, and how fast you use them. Thus, the amount of energy for physical activity varies from one person to another.

In addition to expressing the amount of energy received from food, the term *Calorie* also expresses the amount of energy the body expends during activities. Walking requires more Calories than lying in front of the television. Running at a seven mile per hour pace expends more Calories than walking at four miles an hour. The following chart lists the energy (Calorie) expenditures of different physical activities for a person weighing 150 pounds.

ACTIVITY	CALORIES EXPENDED PER HOUR
Lying down	80
Sitting	100
Golf	250
Walking (4 mph)	300
Softball	360
Tennis (singles)	420
Bicycling (10 mph)	540
Running (7 mph)	840

Chart 6-1

While basal metabolic rate stays within a narrow range for people of the same body size, sex, and age, physical activity varies greatly from one person to the next. Total caloric requirements are therefore determined by your BMR and your activity level.

Determining Your Calorie Needs

To have an adequate energy supply, it is important to balance the amount of food you eat with the energy used for BMR and physical activity. In other words, you must balance Calorie input (food) with Calorie output (BMR and physical activity). The energy balance system of Calorie input-Calorie output is shown in Illustration 6-1.

Illus. 6-1

How can you determine your total Calorie requirements? There are several methods you can use. Computer programs have been designed to figure Calorie expenditure. Personal information such as age, sex, height, and weight is entered into the computer. A record of daily activities is also keyed in. The program then computes the daily caloric requirement. Your teacher may have one of these programs and can show you how it is used.

Several shortcut methods can also help you estimate caloric requirements. The method shown here is adapted from the information in the Recommended Daily Dietary Allowances. It is based upon sex, age, and moderate activity levels. (If you are extremely active, your Calorie needs may be higher than the estimate.) Use your present weight and the information from the accompanying chart. By completing the formula, you will be able to estimate your daily Calorie requirements.

Present weight   x   Calories needed   =   Estimated Calorie needs
  per pound   per day

_____   x   _____   =   _____

CALORIES PER POUND

FEMALES:		MALES:	
Age:	Calories per Pound	Age	Calories per Pound
11-14	25	11-14	29
15-18	18	15-18	22
19-22	16	19-22	20
Adult	15	Adult	17

Chart 6-2

Energy is never lost. The Calories from the food that you eat are either used up by your body or are stored in your body. If you eat more Calories than you spend for physical activity, the extra Calories are stored as body fat. Just the opposite happens when you expend more Calories than you consume. You use body fat to supply the extra energy you need[4].

---

[4] Chart compiled from information in McArdle, Katch, F., and Katch, V. Exercise Physiology: Energy, Nutrition, and Human Performance. Philadelphia: Lea Febiger, 1981

Foods For Energy

If you balance the amount of food you eat with your energy needs, does it make any difference what kinds of food you eat? Yes, it does, and it could make a big difference in your level of performance. Of the three energy nutrients--carbohydrate, fat, and protein--carbohydrate is the main fuel for physical activity. Your body uses glucose for immediate energy during the first few minutes of activity. As the activity continues, the body then begins to use its glycogen stores. Hard training day after day depletes the body's glycogen supply, since only small amounts are stored in the muscles and liver. Once you have used your glycogen stores, you must replace them. Glycogen can be replaced by eating carbohydrate foods. If you do not replenish your glycogen supply, you will feel tired and stale. The results will be poor performance.

Fat can also be used for energy. However, it is less efficient than carbohydrate, since it requires more oxygen to burn. Fat is used as a fuel along with glycogen mainly in endurance events. These events are usually of moderate intensity and/or long duration. Examples are running, especially the marathon, cross country skiing, and distance events in swimming and bicycling. Fat is seldom used as a fuel for high intensity and/or short duration activities, such as sprint events and field events.

Protein can also be used for energy, since it provides Calories. However, the body uses protein for energy only if carbohydrate and fat intake is too low to provide adequate fuel. When protein is used for energy, there is usually a loss of muscle tissue and a loss of strength.

Fuel Balance

How do you balance carbohydrate, fat, and protein intake to have the right kinds of fuel? It is recommended that about 55% of your Calories should come from carbohydrate, 30% from fat, and 15% from protein. Many athletes make the mistake of not eating enough carbohydrates on a daily basis. If you train hard while eating a low carbohydrate diet, you will soon feel tired and sluggish. A diet that contains mainly fat and protein will not replenish glycogen supplies. When glycogen is low, fatigue is the result. Therefore, the diet of extremely active athletes should be composed of 60 to 70% carbohydrate. This increased carbohydrate intake allows the liver and muscles to store adequate amounts of glycogen.

To increase the carbohydrate level in your diet, you should eat more than the minimum number of recommended servings from the Bread, Vegetable and Fruit Groups. Fill your fuel tank with foods like these that are high in carbohydrates:

BREAD-CEREALS:	FRUITS-VEGETABLES:
Breads	Bananas
Bagels	Dried fruits
Muffins	Fruit juices
Cereals	Potatoes
Pastas	Corn
Rice	Squash

Beware of eating too many foods from the Fats and Sweets Group. Although the foods in this group supply carbohydrate in the form of refined sugars, they are high in fat and low in other nutrients. It's best to get your energy from high-grade fuels--breads, cereals, fruits, and vegetables--rather than from low-grade fuels found in Fats and Sweets Group.

Along with additional servings from the Bread and the Vegetable and Fruit Groups, you should include at least three servings from the Milk Group and two Servings from the Meat Group. The servings from these two groups will supply sufficient amounts of protein and fat. If you follow these guidelines, you will be close to the recommended percentages for fuel balance.

Selecting High Energy Foods

Learning to select energy foods may take a little practice. Which would be a better food combination for breakfast to meet an athlete's energy needs?

MENU A: (590 Calories)	*MENU B*: (595 Calories)
1 glass (6 oz.) orange juice	1 medium banana
2 scrambled eggs	1 bowl cornflakes with ½ cup 2% milk
2 slices toast with margarine	2 slices toast with margarine
1 glass (8 oz.) 2% milk	1 glass (8 oz.) 2% milk

If you selected breakfast menu B, you are correct. It is much higher in carbohydrate (62%) but still has adequate amounts of protein (13%) and fat (25%). Menu A is high in fat (44%) but relatively low in carbohydrate (38%). Since carbohydrate is the preferred fuel source, Menu B is the better energy meal.

An easy way to tell if a meal is high in carbohydrates is to check the number of servings from the Bread Group and Vegetable and Fruit Groups. Both Menus A and B have one serving from the Fruit Group. Menu A has two servings from the Bread Group, but Menu B has three servings. The additional serving from the Bread Group in Menu B helps raise the carbohydrate content of this meal.

Food composition charts and the information on nutrition labels also can help you calculate the sources of your Calories. Let's take a look at this example. You're hungry and want something for a quick snack. Would a chocolate covered granola bar be a good high carbohydrate snack?

The nutrition label shows that the granola bar contains 200 Calories and 3 grams of protein, 22 grams of carbohydrate, and 11 grams of fat. There are twice as many grams of carbohydrate as there are grams of fat. At first glance it would seems as if the granola bar is high in carbohydrate.

However, we want to compare Calories rather than grams. To do this multiply the number of grams by the calories per gram.

3 gr. protein	22 gr. carbohydrate	11 gr. fat
x 4 Cal.	x 4 Cal.	x 9 Cal.
12 Calories from protein	88 Calories from carbohydrate	99 Calories from fat

When you compare the Calories, there are more Calories from fat than from carbohydrate. In fact, almost half of the Calories are from fat! Therefore, the granola bar is not a high carbohydrate energy source since there are more Calories from fat than from carbohydrate. Activity Challenge I in the workbook will give you more practice in comparing nutrient sources of Calories.

Personal Diet Analysis

Now that you have learned about nutrients and Calories, the next step is to take a closer look at what you eat. The best way to do this is to keep a daily food "scorecard" for a week. On the food scorecards you will record the foods you ate or drank for breakfast, lunch, dinner, and snacks. You should also list the number and size of the servings you ate.

When you portion out foods such as cereals, milk, and fruit juices, your concept of serving size may be different from the serving size listed on the labels or food composition charts. Just for fun, take some time at home or in class to measure out what you consider to be a typical portion of ready-to-eat breakfast cereal. Select three different kinds: a granola-type cereal, a flaked cereal, and a puffed or square-shaped cereal. For each variety of cereal, pour the serving size you would normally eat into bowls the size you usually use. Then, using a measuring cup, measure the amount of each cereal you poured and compare your serving sizes with the serving sizes listed on the nutrition labels. If your portion size of the granola-type cereal is two times larger than that listed on the label, you are getting two times the Calories and two times the nutrients listed on the label. Try the same experiment for milk and fruit juice to see how accurately you can judge portion size.

Some of the more common serving sizes and nutrient equivalents are listed in Chart 6-3.

BREAD GROUP: (Nutrient equivalents to 1 slice bread)	1 slice bread 1 dinner roll, muffin, biscuit ½ hamburger or hot dog bun ½ bagel or English Muffin 1 cup (1 ounce) dry cereal ½ cup cooked cereal or grits ½ cup cooked rice ½ cup cooked pasta 2 graham cracker squares 5 saltine crackers
VEGETABLE GROUP:	½ cup cooked or choped raw vegetables 1 cup raw leafy vegetables ¾ cup vegetable juice

FRUIT GROUP:	1 medium-sized piece fruit 1 melon wedge ½ cup chopped, cooked, or canned fruit ¼ cup dried fruit ¾ cup (6 oz.) fruit juice
MILK GROUP: (Calcium equivalents to 1 cup milk)	1 cup (8 oz.) milk 1 cup yogurt 1½ oz. natural cheese (Cheddar, Swiss) 2 oz. processed cheese
MEAT GROUP: (Protein equivalents to 2 oz. meat)	2 oz. cooked meat, fish or poultry 4 tablespoons peanut butter 1 cup cooked dired beans or peas 2 eggs

Chart 6-3

After you have recorded the foods and serving sizes you ate, you are ready to complete your analysis. To check Calorie balance, find the number of Calories each food contains. Labels, Calorie charts, and books will be helpful. Finish your analysis by classifying foods into the proper food groups to see if you have received the recommended servings. For directions on keeping your daily food scorecard, turn to Activity Challenge II in the workbook.

There are also several computer programs that will calculate the Calorie and nutrient content of your diet for you. If you have access to one of these programs, follow the program directions and complete your analysis using the computer.

Even though you have learned about the importance of nutrient and caloric balance, you should not make any changes in your eating habits during the week you keep your food scorecards. You want your food record to reflect your *present* eating patterns and food selection habits. The time to make any changes in your diet will come a little later, after you finish this activity.

After completing your diet analysis, you will be one step closer to developing an eating plan for an active teenager.

CHAPTER SUMMARY--CASE STUDY

Re-read the Case Study that introduced this chapter. Using the information in this chapter, what advice would you give Mike?

1. What is used to measure the energy that is found in foods?

2. What two factors determine a person's total energy needs? Explain to Mike why he has been eating more since he started training for the triathlon.

3. If Mike is 18 years old and weighs 155 pounds, approximately how many Calories does he need each day? Why might he need more Calories than this estimated amount?

4. What nutrient is the main energy source that Mike needs for training? How does this nutrient work to provide energy?

5. What percentages of Mike's Calories should come from carbohydrate, fat, and protein?

6. Which food groups are good sources of high quality carbohydrates for Mike?

7. Explain to Mike how to keep a food scorecard for a week. How would keeping a food scorecard be of benefit to him?

7 THE BASIC DIET-- HUNGRY FOR SUCCESS

CASE STUDY

I started attending an exercise class at the local YMCA/YWCA. One evening we had a program on nutrition after class. The title of the program was, "Do You Eat to Live or Live to Eat?" That statement caught my attention. I've always been a person who lives to eat. I'll never pass up an offer of food. As a result, I'm a few pounds too heavy. Generally, I usually don't think too much about the nutritional value of food. If I don't have time to eat a meal, I usually snack on a candy bar, chips, or a soft drink. After hearing the speaker say that nutrition is as much a part of a fitness program as exercise, I've decided that I need to change my attitude. Is there a special diet that I should follow? What kinds of foods do I need to eat? How do I go about breaking my bad eating habits? Any advice you can give me will be helpful.

--Kelly, high school junior

Everyone has advice about nutrition. "Eat sensibly." "Eat three square meals a day." "Cut out rich foods." "Don't snack." Generalizations about diet without explanations are common. So how can you know how much to eat, what to eat, and when to eat? Read on if you're hungry for success.

Diet and Health

Exercising and following a good diet contribute to fitness and good health during the teenage years and on into adulthood. Learning to eat well provides several short-term benefits. One immediate benefit is the effect that diet has on appearance. Proper nutrition helps you maintain an ideal body weight and have healthy skin and hair. Good eating habits also will keep your level of energy high. If you are an athlete, your performance can be affected by the amount of energy you have. A well-planned diet and good eating habits allow you to practice and compete to the best of your ability.

Good nutrition also has the long-term benefit of helping prevent diet-related health problems which often show up later in adulthood. The risk of heart disease and high blood pressure can be reduced by following a nutritious diet and exercising regularly.

Heart disease is influenced by a high intake of dietary fat, especially saturated fat and cholesterol. Saturated fatty acids, which are used for energy, come from animal foods. *Cholesterol* is not used for energy but is a fat-like substance used in many of the body's chemical processes.

There are two sources of cholesterol. Cholesterol is found in foods from animal sources. Meats, fish, poultry, egg yolks, and dairy products all contain cholesterol. In addition to dietary cholesterol, the body can make its own cholesterol.

Most authorities feel that high levels of cholesterol increase the risk of heart attacks. Too much cholesterol causes fatty deposits to build up on the walls of the arteries. When the arteries become blocked, a heart attack can occur.

To help reduce the risk of heart disease, eat fewer foods that are high in cholesterol and saturated fat. (Saturated fats have been found to raise blood cholesterol levels). When selecting foods, choose lean meats and trim off any visible fat. Eat more poultry and fish. Limit eggs to three or four a week. Use margarine and vegetable oils rather than butter. Select low-fat milk, yogurt, and cheese.

Hypertension or high blood pressure is another health problem which is often diet-related. Blood pressure is a measure of the force with which the heart pumps blood through the arteries. When a person has high blood pressure, the heart has to work harder to pump blood through the arteries.

Too much sodium in the diet may contribute to high blood pressure in some people who are sensitive to salt. The safe and adequate amount of sodium that is recommended is ½ to 1½ teaspoons per day. The average sodium intake of Americans is 2½ teaspoons per day, with many people consuming even higher amounts.

Cutting down on salt is a healthy dietary change that many people could make. To do this, reduce salt in cooking and add little or no salt at the table. Limit intake of salty processed foods like canned soups, lunchmeats, and snack foods.

The Basic Diet

How can you plan a diet for both short-term and long-term benefits? The *BASIC DIET* is the answer. There is no one special diet that everyone must follow. *The basic diet is a series of guidelines about how to eat on a day-by-day basis for the rest of your life.* The success of the basic diet is that it can be altered to suit the individual. It allows for personal preference and provides a variety of ways to meet both nutrient and caloric requirements.

Allowing for individual preferences is important. So you don't like lima beans? Choose corn instead. You can't eat strawberries because you're allergic to them ? Select another fruit, maybe cantaloupe. Ham just doesn't digest well? Have turkey as your meat selection. Since no single food supplies all the necessary nutrients, you can select from among a variety of foods to meet your nutritional requirements.

The basic diet also allows for differences in caloric intake. Calorie requirements vary greatly from one athlete to another, because of body size and sex. Calorie needs are also greater druing the training and competitive seasons, because increased activity places higher energy demands on the body. During the "off" season, you usually require fewer Calories. The basic diet allows flexibility for meeting these changing caloric needs.

What kind of diet plan permits such diversity? There is no special diet to follow--no list of foods you must eat or eliminate, no specified number of meals to eat each day. The basic diet incorporates two general sets of guidelines--one covering food selection and the other covering eating patterns. Let's take a closer look at the guidelines for each area.

Food Choices

You should select foods for your daily food "lineup" from the Food Guide Pyramid. The minimum number of recommended servings from the five main food groups provide the nutrients you need and about 1,600 Calories. However, most teenagers require more than 1,600 Calories a day. Teenaged girls usually need about 2,200 Calories and teenaged boys require at least 2,800 Calories per day. Teens who are physically active may need even more Calories to meet their energy demands. Teenagers should aim for the number of servings recommended in the chart below to meet their daily caloric requirements.

Teen Girls	Food Group	Teen Boys
9	Bread	11
4	Vegetable	5
3	Fruit	4
3	Milk	3
2	Meat	3

Designing your daily food "line-up" is easy. The sample food "line-ups" show you how this is done.

2200 CAL LINE-UP

Breakfast:	Calories:
½ grapefruit	45
Cereal (1 cup)	110
¼ cup 2% milk	60
1 slice toast	75
Margarine (1 pat)	35
Jelly (1 teaspoon)	25
1 cup 2% milk	120
	470

Lunch:	
Hamburger sandwich	
Meat patty (3 oz)	185
Bun	120
1 cup vegetable soup	80
Saltine crackers	60
Grapes	55
1 cup low-fat chocolate milk	180
	680

2800 CAL LINE-UP

Breakfast:	Calories:
½ grapefruit	45
Cereal (1 cup) with	110
¼ cup 2% milk	60
2 slices toast	150
Margarine (2 pats)	70
Jelly (1 Tablespoon)	55
1 cup 2% milk	120
	610

Lunch:	
Hamburger sandwich	
Meat patty (3 oz.)	185
Bun	120
1 cup vegetable soup	80
Saltine Crackers	60
Grapes	55
1 cup low-fat chocolate milk	180
2 oatmeal cookies	135
	815

Dinner:		Dinner:	
Baked fish (3 oz.)	135	Baked fish (3 ounces)	135
Baked potato	150	Baked potato	150
Margarine	70	Margarine	70
Tossed Salad (1 cup)	20	Tossed salad (1 cup)	20
Dressing (2 tbsp.)	130	Dressing (2 tbsps.)	130
Green beans (¼ cup)	15	Green Beans (¼ cup)	15
Plain Muffin	120	Plain muffin	120
Margarine	35	Margarine	35
½ cup fresh fruit		½ cup fresh fruit	
salad	100	salad	100
1 cup 2% milk	120	1 cup 2% milk	120
	895		895
Snacks:		Snacks:	
1 apple	85	Peanut butter sandwich	
½ cup frozen yogurt	90	Peanut butter	190
	175	2 slices bread	150
		1 cup frozen yogurt	180
			520
Total Calories--	2200	Total Calories--	2840

2200 CAL LINE-UP		2800 CAL LINE-UP
6 servings	BREAD GROUP	9 servings
4 servings	VEGETABLE GROUP	4 servings
4 servings	FRUIT GROUP	3 servings
4 servings	MILK GROUP	4½ servings
2 servings	MEAT GROUP	3 servings

These suggested Calorie levels may need to be adjusted for some people with different levels of physical activity. Some females who have a low activity level may require fewer Calories (about 2,000) per day. On the other hand, males who are extremely active may need closer to 3,500 Calories per day. (With a little experimentation, you should soon learn how to choose foods that provide the right nutrient and caloric balance you need.)

Now turn to Activity Challenge I in the workbook and plan a sample food line-up that meets your nutritional and caloric needs. When you make your food choices, select foods that you like. Also, try to include low-fat dairy products and don't overdo on foods that are high in saturated fats. (Be sure to meet the requirements from the five major food groups in the Food Pyramid before adding too many foods from the Fats and Sweets Group.)

Eating Patterns

Poor eating patterns can affect the energy levels of an active person. Habits, busy schedules, and group pressures can lead to skipped breakfasts, erratic meal times, and poor snacking rituals. Establishing sound eating habits while you are young is easier than breaking poor ones later in life.

Many persons make it a habit to skip breakfast. Starting the day on an empty fuel tank doesn't make sense. Eating food in the morning to fuel your body for the rest of the day does makes sense. Learn to be a breakfast eater.

The ideal meal pattern is to eat three meals per day on a regular schedule. However, individual activities often disrupt family meal schedules, and eating becomes hit-or-miss. Learning how to schedule meals into the day's routine is beneficial. Instead of eating three larger meals, it might be easier for you to eat five smaller meals during the day.

Snacks are a way to get from one meal to the next. Whether snacks are good or bad for you depends on your snacking habits. Snack foods which have little nutritional value and are high in Calories can add unwanted pounds. If snacks are eaten too close to meals, they can prevent hunger for more nutritious foods. However, on days when you miss meals due to school activities, practice, or work, snacks can take the place of the meal you miss. In this case, think of snacks as "mini-meals," which include foods from the Food Pyramid Groups.

Learning to eat breakfast, planning regular meals that fit your schedule, and snacking wisely are eating patterns that are especially important for athletes and active people.

Break-the-Fast

Breakfast is the most important meal of the day. It literally means to "break the fast." Would you volunteer to give up food for 18 hours? Probably not. Yet, this is what you do by skipping breakfast. Let's say that the last meal you ate on Tuesday was a 6 o'clock dinner. You worked from 7 o'clock to 10 o'clock., so you missed your evening TV snack. Since you got to bed later than usual, you slept-in an extra half an hour and missed breakfast. The next chance you had to eat was at noon on Wednesday. Yes, you just volunteered not to eat for 18 hours!

Why eat breakfast? If you eat breakfast, you will be more mentally and physically alert. Breakfast boosts the level of glucose that the brain and central nervous system need to function. Low glucose levels cause "mid-morning slump", which is characterized by drowsiness, headache, and stomach "rumblings." For an athlete, breakfast is even more important. The carbohydrates eaten at breakfast provide fuel for after-school practices and competitions. By not "filling-up" in the morning, you will be running close to empty by the end of the day. Your work ouput will be less, mental reactions will be slower, and muscular fatigue will be greater.

Breakfast-skippers have all kinds of excuses. Do any of these sound familiar? "I'm not hungry in the morning." Did you eat a whole bag of potato chips and drink too much soda before going to bed? Eating during the daytime when you need fuel makes more sense than sleeping on it. Snack lightly at night; you'll feel more like eating in the morning.

"If I eat in the morning, I get sick." Teach yourself to eat breakfast, but don't start by eating a huge meal. Give your body time to adjust by gradually introducing foods over a period of time. Begin by eating lightly--a small glass of orange juice and one slice of toast. Once you adjust to this intake, try adding a bowl of cereal. Before long, breakfast will be a part of your daily routine.

"I don't have enough time in the morning." So you'd rather have an extra half-an-hour of sleep? A "quickie" breakfast is just what you need. Many recipes take very little preparation or can be prepared the night before. Try a blender breakfast which contains milk or yogurt and fruit. You can make breakfast spreads for toast, bagels, or muffins from cheeses, peanut butter, and fruits. The combinations are unlimited. If you're really in a pinch for time, grab a "carry-out" breakfast and eat on the run. Have a couple of breakfast cookies full of cereal, nuts, and cheese along with a can of fruit juice.

"I hate breakfast foods." Then be creative and try something new. Any nutritious food is all right for breakfast--even last night's left-over pizza! Use muffins, bagels, and frozen waffles to prepare special breakfast treats. And don't forget about sandwiches--especially peanut butter or grilled cheese.

Activity Challenge II in the workbook contains ideas for breakfast-skippers' breakfasts. Try these recipes either at school or at home. They'll provide the nutrients and energy you need to start the day with a full fuel tank. A little thought, a little imagination, and a little planning are all you need to start your day right!

Eating On-the-Go

Because of time commitments, you may find it almost impossible to fit the traditional meals--breakfast, lunch, and dinner--into your busy schedule. You should try to eat regular meals that provide a variety of foods, but meal hours can be flexible to fit your schedule. The main concern is meeting nutritional and caloric needs throughout the day. Skipping meals can often lead to snacking on high Calorie, low nutrient foods, which may meet caloric needs but not nutrient needs. Rather than eating three large meals, you may find it easier to eat several small meals. Small meals provide more nutrients than a quick snack, but do not require a lot of accompanying foods or take much time to prepare. Do you usually skip lunch? At 10 o'clock munch on some crackers with peanut butter for a mid-morning pick-up. Then in the middle of the afternoon have yogurt and an apple. The one thing to remember is "what you eat is more important than when you eat." Follow the recommendations of the Food Guide Pyramid for food selection and vary the number and size of meals to fit your schedule.

Today, family members lead more independent lives. Since individual activities may interfere with meals, family members often eat alone at home. Many teenagers are responsible for preparing their own meals when they get home from practice or work.

Preparing nutritious meals does not have to be time consuming. The object is to prepare foods that are quick and easy. Try preparing combination foods. Sandwiches aren't hard to make, and you'll have foods from the Meat and the Bread Groups. Add lettuce and tomato slices for a serving from the Vegetable Group. Tacos and muffin pizzas (see recipe in Activity Challenge IV) are also good combination foods that are easy to prepare.

The microwave oven is a real time-saver. Raid the refrigerator. If you find leftovers from last night's supper, reheat them in the microwave. Baked potatoes are a snap to prepare in the microwave. Add some toppings like broccoli (also cooked in the microwave) and cheese (melted in the microwave) for a quick mini-meal.

People with busy schedules frequently eat meals away from home. When eating out it is usually more difficult to make good food choices than when eating at home. Fast-food restaurants are favorite places for quick meals. Eating frequently at fast-food restaurants can create dietary problems. Most fast foods are high in fat and high in sodium. They are also high in Calories. It's easy to consume 1000 Calories or more in one sitting if you are not careful.

If you choose foods wisely, you can get a well balanced meal at a fast food restaurant. More choices are now available to health-conscious eaters. Instead of a large order of French fries, select a baked potato. Side salads and salad bars can be good choices. A basic hamburger is better for you than the bacon deluxe. The bacon adds little more than saturated fat and unnecessary Calories.

There are also differences in the way fast-food restaurants prepare foods. Some restaurants prepare their French fries in beef tallow or lard, which is high in unhealthy saturated fat. Other restaurants advertise that they cook their fries in vegetable oil, which contains unsaturated fat. Some chains char-broil their burgers while others fry them. Making wise fast-food choices can provide you with a quick but nutritious meal.

Empty Calorie Snacks

Mention the work "snack" and what comes to mind? Soft drinks, candy bars, potato chips, or an apple, pizza, ice cream? Eating between meals is not harmful if you need extra Calories to meet daily caloric requirements. In fact, if they are properly chosen, snacks are very important for active athletes. The idea, then, is not to eliminate snacks but to make changes in the types of foods often selected for snacks. Typical snack foods usually contain lots of "empty" calories. "Empty calorie" foods are high in Calories but low in nutrients. Most of these foods are highly processed. During processing many ingredients such as refined sugars, salt, and fat are added. Because little nutritional value remains, most snack foods belong in the Fats and Sweets Group.

You know that desserts, candies, and soft drinks contain large amounts of sugar. In fact, there are seven to twelve teaspoons of sugar in a 12 ounce soft drink! Other processed foods such as catsup, lunch meats, and salad dressings contain substantial amounts of "hidden" sweeteners. Ingredient labels on food packages can help you find these "hidden" forms of sugar. Look for corn syrup or corn sweetener, fructose, dextrose, honey, brown sugar, and molasses on the ingredient list. Ingredients are listed by weight in descending order, from most to least. If one of these sweeteners is listed as the first or second ingredient, it's safe to assume that lots of sugar has been added.

Contrary to popular belief, molasses and honey are really not nutritionally superior to white sugar. White sugar and honey are both digested into the same simple sugars, glucose and fructose. The fructose is further broken down into glucose before it can be used for energy. The amounts of vitamins and minerals found in honey are insignificant.

Learn to become a sugar sleuth by completing Activity Challenge III in the workbook.

Empty calorie foods may also be high in fat, which is either added as an ingredient or is used for cooking. As an example, let's see what happens to a potato as it is processed into potato chips. A potato that is boiled or baked is an excellent complex carbohydrate source and contains only a trace of fat. By the time processing is complete, potato chips are 40% fat and highly salted, with little left of the potato's orginial nutritional value.

Many of the fats used in processed foods are high in saturated fats. Ingredient labels will tell you what type of fats have been used in processing. Most fats that are liquid at room temperature contain unsaturated fatty acids and are better for you than solid fats such as lard and butter. However, beware of coconut oil, palm oil, and palm kernel oil. These three oils are very high in unhealthy saturated fats. They are commonly found in snack crackers, cookies, coffee whiteners, and whipped toppings. Checking the ingredient labels will help you avoid products that are high in saturated fats.

Processed foods are also high in sodium. Typical sources of sodium are food additives that contain the word sodium. Examples are sodium nitrite, which is used in bacon and ham. Monosodium glutamate is added to foods to enhance flavor. Salt is also used as an ingredient in many processed foods. Canned soups and vegetables, TV dinners, lunchmeats, and condiments, such as catsup and mustard, contain substantial amounts of salt. Reading ingredients labels will help you determine how much sodium has been added. Many low-sodium products are now available. Look for reduced sodium soups and vegetables. Some snack foods such as crackers, chips, and pretzels are available in unsalted versions.

Changing Snack Habits

Empty calorie foods are easy to obtain, convenient to eat on the run, and appealing to the taste-buds. The main problem is that they often replace more nutritious foods in meals and snacks. You don't have to give up your favorite snacks, but you might decide to eat less of them than you usually do. Rather than drinking two cans of soft drinks a day, limit yourself to one. If you can't stay away from potato chips, buy an individual-sized package. That way, even if you polish off the whole bag, it's not like devouring the one-pound size!

There's another easy change that you can make in your snacking habits. Replace some of your snack foods from the Fats and Sweets Group with foods from the major Food Pyramid groups. Food substitutions will help you meet both caloric and *nutrient* needs. Instead of candy, try dried fruit and nut mixes. Substitute blueberry muffins or banana bread for cake. Fruit juices are an excellent replacement for soft drinks. Oatmeal cookies with raisins and nuts have more nutritional value than plain sugar cookies.

Preparing Your Own Snacks

You can also make your own snack foods rather than buying processed varieties. This way you can control both the ingredients and the cooking. It's easy to cut down on sugar. In most recipes you can reduce the amount of sugar by ⅓ to ½. If an oatmeal cookie recipe calls for 1 cup of sugar, try using ⅔ cup or ½ cup instead. More healthful ingredients can be used when you do your own cooking. For example, if your recipe uses 2 cups of flour, use one cup of white flour and one cup of whole wheat flour. Increase nutritional value by adding raisins and nuts to cookies. Use low-fat dairy products rather than whole-milk products to reduce fat content. Instead of frying foods, bake, if you can, to lower the fat content. A baked sweet roll is a better choice than a deep-fried doughnut.

Converting a favorite recipe into a more healthful version is not difficult. Using some of the suggestions given above, the following recipe for Apple Cinnamon Muffins has been revised from the original version. The amounts of sugar and salt have been reduced. Low-fat milk and vegetable oil lower the amount of saturated fat in the muffins. Nuts are an optional ingredient that can be added to increase nutritional value. These changes are shown in italics.

APPLE CINNAMON MUFFINS

ORIGINAL:	REVISED:
2 c. sifted flour	2 c. sifted flour
½ c. sugar	¼ c. sugar
1 Tbsp. baking powder	1 Tbsp. baking powder
1 tsp. salt	½ tsp. salt
2 tsp. cinnamon	2 tsp. cinnamon
1 egg, slightly beaten	1 egg, slightly beaten
¾ c. milk	¾ c. low-fat or skim milk
3 Tbsp. butter, melted	3 Tbsp. vegetable oil
1 c. finely chopped apples	1 c. finely chopped apples
	¼ c. chopped nuts (optional)

Mix first five ingredients together in large mixing bowl. In another bowl mix egg, milk, vegetable oil, and chopped apples. Add liquid ingredients to dry ingredients. Stir just until mixed. (The batter will be lumpy.) Fold in nuts, if desired. Fill greased muffin cups ⅔ full. Bake at 400 for 15 to 20 minutes or until lightly browned. To reduce cholesterol content, use two egg whites instead of one whole egg.

Snacking wisely means keeping an eye on the main goal--a balanced diet, both in nutrients and Calories. Snacking can be beneficial for you if you select your snacks carefully. Activity Challenge IV in the workbook contains recipes for snacks that you can whip up in the kitchen at school or at home. Keep these ideas in mind the next time you have a snack attack!

Scoring Your Diet and Eating Habits

To review the guidelines of the basic diet: Do you use the Food Pyramid to plan meals? Do you eat breakfast? Do you eat regular meals that fit your time schedule? Do you snack wisely? To answer these questions, turn to Activity Challenge V in the workbook. As part of this activity you will analyze your food choices and eating patterns. To do this you will need the Daily Food Scorecards from Activity Challenge II in Chapter Six of your workbook.

By looking at your food scorecards, you should see if any patterns in food choices and eating habits show up. To evaluate food choices for nutritional value, check the total number of servings you ate from each of the food groups. Do you average only one serving from the Milk Group? If this is the case, you may not be getting enough calcium. You can also use your food scorecards to identify specific eating habits. Do you often skip meals? How often do you snack, and when do you snack?

Once you detect patterns in food choices and eating habits, you can decide if you need to make any changes. For example, if you don't drink milk, you might pay closer attention to choosing other calcium-rich foods. If you skip lunch because you don't like cafeteria food, you could try packing your lunch.

Nutrition goals, like your fitness goals, are personal. Although they may be similar to the goals of others, you need to design a plan that will help you meet your goals.

When you begin to set nutrition goals, recognize the good eating patterns that you have. Your first goal is to keep your positive eating patterns. Looking at the good things you do helps prevent you from becoming discouraged.

Your second goal is to change poor eating patterns. When you have decided what changes you want to make, write them down in order of importance to you. Then decide *how* you are going to achieve your goal. It's easier to make changes if you have a plan of action to follow.

Let's use Jim as an example. When Jim looked at his food scorecards, he saw that he always ate breakfast. His first goal was to keep his good breakfast habit. However, Jim noticed that he ate a lot of processed foods that were high in sodium. For snacks, he usually ate potato chips, corn chips, and other highly salted snack foods. Jim also realized that he always added extra salt to his food. Once Jim picked up the pattern of a high sodium intake, he decided he should reduce the amount of salt in his diet. Jim's plan of action to reduce salt included two things. He would eat only one salty snack food a day and would try not to add extra salt to his food.

When you have completed Activity Challenge V, you will have developed a set of personal nutrition goals. Following this nutrition game plan will help you improve your food choices and eating habits.

"Training" Your Appetite

Making changes in your eating patterns is not easy. It takes work and motivation to achieve your goals. Others can give you encouragement, but you have to make the changes yourself.

Working to condition yourself nutritionally is just as hard as conditioning yourself physically.

How do you "train your appetite" to meet the goals of your "newtrition" game plan? Be realistic and don't change too much too fast. Rather than trying to break all of your bad habits at once, target in on one habit at a time. Wait until you're sure the first problem is under control before you tackle another. You'll be sure to develop "withdrawal" cravings if you give up your favorite "empty calorie" snacks by going "cold turkey." Gradually reduce the amounts you eat. Instead of six chocolate chip cookies for an after-school snack, cut your ration to three. Eat one dish of chunky chocolate ice cream rather than the whole gallon! Remember you've had a long time to develop these habits, so don't expect a complete change overnight. To learn how to use these ideas when "training your appetiite," turn to Activity Challenge VI in the workbook.

If you're hungry for success, you should take a good look at your food choices and eating habits. If what you see doesn't fit the guidelines of the basic diet, it's up to you to make the changes. A good basic diet on a day-by-day basis is important for everyone's appearance and health. If you are an athlete, following a good nutrition gameplan is even more important. It will help you perform to the best of your ability.

CHAPTER SUMMARY--CASE STUDY

Re-read the Case Study that introduced this chapter. Using the information in this chapter, what advice would you give Kelly?

1. What are the immediate benefits that Kelly should be able to see from a good diet?
   What is a long-term benefit of a good diet?

2. Why should Kelly try to eat fewer food that are high in cholesterol and saturated fat?
   List four foods that contain cholesterol.

3. Explain to Kelly why too much sodium can cause problems for some people.
   Name four foods that have a high sodium content.

4. Explain the guidelines of the BASIC DIET to Kelly.

5. What are three good eating patterns that Kelly should try to develop?

6. Why is breakfast especially important now that Kelly has started going to an exercise class?

7. Explain this statement to Kelly: "What you eat is more important than when you eat."

8. How can learning to read ingredient labels help Kelly make good food choices?

9. Why is it important for Kelly to work on changing only one habit at a time?

8 IT'S ALL A MATTER OF BALANCE-- PRINCIPLES of WEIGHT CONTROL

CASE STUDY

I have two children in high school. Matt is a junior and a varsity football player. Jana, a freshman, is taking ballet. Jana was about ten pounds overweight when she started dancing, so she's been trying to lose weight. I'm concerned about her because I almost have to force her to eat. She says that she's never hungry. She won't tell me how much weight she has lost, but her clothes are starting to hang on her. Matt is just the opposite. All I ever hear him saying is, "Mom, I just have to gain some weight." He eats constantly and seems to be a bottomless pit. What advice can you give me about weight control so that I can help my teenagers?

--Julia Johnson, mother

How often have you heard comments like these? "I need to lose five pounds by weigh-in time tomorrow." "Coach says if I gain eight pounds, I'll be a better lineman." "I look good at this weight. Now if I can just keep it there." Finding and maintaining an ideal weight is important for everyone. An extra ten pounds can slow you down, but being ten pounds too light can leave you with little energy.

How can you determine your ideal weight? Active people should determine ideal weight by measuring body fat rather than by using the scale and a height/weight chart. This way you can tell if you are "overfat" rather than "overweight."

Body Composition

There is a difference between being "overweight" and "overfat." *Overweight* simply means that you weigh more than the height/weight charts recommend. *Overfat* indicates that you have more body fat than you should have. Height/weight charts show if you are high in weight compared to others of your age, height, and sex, but they cannot tell you how fat you are. Many athletes are "overweight" because they weigh more than the charts recommend. But when their body fat is measured, most athletes are not "overfat," because their additional weight is from muscle rather than fat. The reverse is sometime true, too. People who do not exercise regularly may be "underweight" according to the charts, but they still may have too much fat and so be "overfat."

A scale measures your *total* body weight, including bones, organs, body fluids, muscles, and fat. It provides little information concerning the *composition* of your body weight. Most people carry extra weight in fat. For athletes, it is better to have more muscle than fat. Since scales do not measure fat, how can you tell if you are overfat?

Under Water Weighing

There are a number of ways to estimate body fat. One of the most sophisticated tests is underwater weighing. This test must be conducted by a trained expert and requires special laboratory equipment--a large tank of water and a chair attached to a special scale. The subject being tested sits in the chair, which is submerged beneath the surface of the water. As the subject lowers his head under the water, he expels as much air as possible from his lungs and then holds his breath for approximately five seconds while his underwater weight is recorded on the scale. This procedure is repeated eight to twelve times because the subject learns to expel more air from his lungs as he becomes more familiar with the testing procedure. The subject's underwater weight (an average of the last two or three trials) is put into a complex mathematical formula which gives an estimate of his percentage of body fat. A nearby university or sportsmedicine clinic may be willing to give underwater weighing demonstrations so that you can see how this test is conducted.

Skinfold Testing

A simpler method for determining body fat uses skinfold measurements. About half of your body fat is located between your skin and muscles, where it can easily be measured. At various sites on the body the skin is pinched together and the underlying fat is pulled away from the muscles. The skin and the fat tissues are then measured with a tool called a skinfold caliper, which measures the skinfold thickness in millimeters. Once the thicknesses of several skinfolds have been determined, the values are plugged into a formula or a chart that converts the skinfold readings into an estimated percentage of body fat.

Activity Challenge I in the workbook gives directions for estimating percentage of body fat using measurements from two sites on the body. For males, the skinfolds are measured below the *subscapula* (shoulder blade) and on the front of the *thigh*. For females, the skinfolds are taken at the *triceps* (back of the arm) and at the top of the *iliac* (pelvic bone). Illustration 8-1 shows the location of each of these sites. Directions in the workbook give detailed information for locating these sites and for using the caliper to measure the skinfolds.

illus 8-1 from workbook p.55

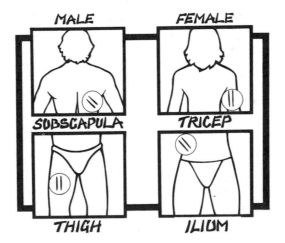

108

Body Fat Levels

How much body fat should you have? The total amount of body fat is found in two major forms. *Storage fat* consists mainly of subcutaneous fat which is stored beneath the skin. Storage fat also includes a small amount of fat deposited around various organs for protection. *Essential fat* is the other form of fat. It is found in nerve tissues, various organs, and bone marrow and is required for normal body functioning. For males 3% body fat is considered to be essential and for females 12% fat is essential. Health-related problems can occur if body fat drops below these essential levels. When percentages of essential fat and storage fat are combined, the body composition of the average high school males should be approximately 15% and the average high school female 23%. Women have a higher percentage of body fat because of their child-bearing role.

For athletes, excess *storage* fat can impair athletic performance. The more fat you have, the more work you do to carry it around. Because athletes perform better if they have a greater proportion of muscle in their body composition, the recommended percentage of body fat for athletes is lower than the 15% for the average teenage male and lower than 23% for the average teenage female. A number of studies conducted on the body composition of athletes show that it is impossible to establish an ideal percentage of body fat, because values differ from one sport to another and even within the same sport. However, most experts recommend that a well-conditioned male athlete in high school have a body fat percentage ranging from 7% to 10%. Well-trained high school females should have body fat levels of 17% to 20%. Athletes involved in gymnastics, distance running, and wrestling generally have body fat percentages at the lower end of these ranges. Baseball and softball players, shot putters and discus throwers, and football linemen are likely to have body fat percentages at the higher end.

Sometimes athletes are eager to compete at a very low weight. Losing too much weight may cause them to drop below the recommended minimum levels of body fat. Below these levels, an athlete does not have enough strength for vigorus activity and runs the risk of upsetting normal body functions. For male athletes in their teens, this recommended minimum is 7%, because of the demands of rapid growth. For female athletes 15% body fat is the recommended minimum. Some females with a very low percentage of body fat may stop menstruating. This condition is known as amenorrhea. A low body fat percentage, as well as low Calorie intake and intense exercise, may contribute to amenorrhea. Female athletes who have amenorrhea may have problems with stress fractures and low bone density. A doctor should be consulted for treatment of amenorrhea.

Determining an Ideal Competition Weight

Once you have estimated your percentage of body fat, it is possible to determine an ideal competition weight. Your ideal weight is how much you would weigh once you have achieved your desired level of body fatness. First, set an acceptable level of body fat for yourself. Look at the recommended percentages and examine your previous levels of performance. For example, if you wrestled well last year at 11% body fat, don't feel you must drop to 7% body fat just becasue it is the lowest recommended value for wrestlers.

By following the four step procedure given below and filling in the blanks with your own personal data, you can estimate your ideal competiton weight.

Step 1:
Desired % body fat for your sport _____ %

Step 2:
Present % body fat - Desired % body fat = % body fat to lose

_____ - _____ = _____

Step 3:
Present weight x % of body fat to lose = Number of pounds to lose (change to decimal)

Step 4:
Present weight - Number of pounds to lose = Ideal weight

After you have achieved your ideal weight, you should have another skin-fold test done. If you have not exercised, you may have lost some muscle tissue as well as fat and as a result may still need to lose more fat. If you have exercised strenuously while trying to lose weight, you may have gained muscle tissue which weighs more than fat. Thus your ideal weight may be higher than you estimated. By using body fat percentage rather than the scale you can determine whether or not you can continue to lose weight safely, since it shows the relationship of body fat and muscle to total body weight.

Principles of Weight Control

Now that you have determined your ideal competition weight, you are ready to start a weight control program. Maybe you're satisfied with your present levels of weight and body fat and just want to maintain them. Perhaps you need to lose both body fat and body weight. On the other hand, you may want to gain weight by adding muscle. Whatever your goals, there are a few concepts that will help you play the "weighting" game.

When working with weight control, Calories *do* count. As you may remember from Chapter Six, foods provide energy which is measured in Calories. This energy is never lost, but rather is used up or stored by the body. Weight control, then, is a matter of energy balance. It is the relationship between energy input (food intake) and energy output (BMR and activity) that creates these equations for weight control:

Weight Maintenance ➝ Energy Input = Energy Output

Weight Loss ➝ Energy Input < Energy Output

Weight Gain ➝ Energy Input > Energy Output

A key figure to remember is 3,500: one pound of fat equals 3,500 Calories. Anytime you take in 3,500 Calories more than you use, you gain one pound. To lose one pound of fat, you must use 3,500 Calories more than you take in.

Losing Weight

Let's apply these principles to a weight control program designed for weight loss. To lose weight, energy input must be less than energy output. For each pound of body fat you want to lose, you must create a 3,500 Calorie deficit. To lose one pound a week, you must create a deficit of 500 Calories per day (3,500 divided by 7 = 500). By creating a 1000 Calorie per day deficit, you will lose two pounds a week. You can achieve a Calorie deficit in one of these three ways:

By eating less

By exercising more
By a combination of the two

Eating less is one way to lose weight. By taking in fewer Calories, your body burns its fat stores for energy. As you burn these fat stores, you will lose weight.

Exercise is another way to lose weight. When you exercise, you burn Calories. Aerobic exercise is the best type of exercise to use for weight loss. With aerobic exercise, your body uses oxygen. Since sufficient oxygen is available, the body can burn fat as energy during aerobic exercise. To burn fat, it is better to exercise for a longer period of time with less intensity than to exercise harder for a shorter period of time. Walking, jogging, bicycling, rowing, swimming, and aerobic dance are all good fat burning exercises. By increasing exercise levels above and beyond your normal training routine, you can lose weight without making any changes in your diet.

A combination of diet and exercise is another method for losing weight. By eating a little less and exercising a little more, you will not have to make drastic alterations in your food intake or energy output. Reducing your caloric intake by 250 Calories per day and increasing your daily exercise so you burn an additional 250 Calories will result in a loss of one pound per week.

For athletes the combination of diet and exercise is the most effective way to reach ideal competition weight. Fat lost through exercise tends to stay off longer than fat lost by dieting alone. Another advantage of increasing exercise is that it makes your body metabolically more active by elevating your body temperature. Even after you stop exercising, your BMR remains elevated for several hours. Your body then continues to burn Calories at a more rapid rate until your body temperature returns to normal. One problem of losing weight by dieting without exercise is the loss of muscle tissue as well as fat. Since a high proportion of muscle to fat is important for performance, athletes must be careful to lose body weight by reducing the amount of fat rather than muscle.

Let's see how the diet/exercise combination works in a weight loss program. Susan is a cross country runner who needs to lose five pounds to reach her ideal competition weight. Her normal caloric requirement to meet her daily energy needs is 2,200 Calories. To lose one pound a week, she needs to create a 500 Calorie deficit per day, so she plans to increase her activity by 250 Calories and cut her food intake by 250 Calories. Susan gets up earlier and runs for 20 minutes before school, thus burning the extra 250 Calories. To create the 250 Calorie deficit in food intake, Susan needs to make a few minor changes in her food selection. Instead of drinking chocolate milk with her lunch, she switches to 2% lowfat milk. This substitution save 80 Calories. At dinner she uses two tablespoons of low-calorie French dressing on her tossed salad rather than regular dressing for a savings of another 70 Calories. For an evening snack she eats two chocolate chip cookies instead of the usual four and saves another 100 Calories. If she follows this plan for five weeks, Susan should reach her ideal competition weight easily and safely.

Once you decide which method you wish to use to create your calorie deficit, there are several other guidelines you should keep in mind. First, you should try to lose weight *before* your competitive season begins, so plan ahead. Keep in mind that you can *safely* lose one to two pounds a week. This way your weight loss will be in body fat. If you lose weight at a faster rate, you will begin losing muscle as well as fat. As a result, your performance will suffer. If you need to lose ten pounds, allow five to ten weeks to reach your goal. Don't try to lose ten pounds in two weeks!

Even though you want to lose weight, do not *drastically* reduce your caloric intake. If you do, you will lack the energy and strength to train. During the training and competitive season, males need *at least* 2,000 Calories to meet their energy needs, and females need no fewer than 1,700 Calories each day--another reason why a weight loss program should begin before the start of the competitive season.

To keep track of your weight loss, weigh yourself once a week at the same time of the day. It is preferable to weigh without clothing first thing in the morning. If you weigh youself every day, you may become discouraged because of fluctuations caused by water retention or food residue in the digestive tract. It is highly unlikely that you will lose a pound of fat in a single day! About once a month, you should have another skinfold test done to re-measure your body fat. If you are losing weight properly, your percentage of body fat should be decreasing as well as your scale weight. Remember that if you are exercising as well as dieting, you may be increasing muscle while losing fat. Since muscle weighs more than fat your weight may not drop as much as expected. However, this shift in body composition will probably add strength and improve your performance.

The basic diet, which was discussed in Chapter Seven, can be used when planning a reduced Calorie diet for weight loss. You will first need to determine how many Calories you need each day. (See chart on page 84 in Chapter 6.) Start with the number of Calories needed to meet your daily energy requirements. Then *subtract* the number of Calories to create the deficit necessary to meet your weekly weight loss goal. Increase your exercise and reduce your caloric intake accordingly. Meeting these reduced caloric requirements will be easier if you follow these hints:

TRY TO EAT AT LEAST THREE MEALS PER DAY, ESPECIALLY BREAKFAST. If you skip breakfast, you will probably create a caloric deficit that may cause you to "pig-out" later in the day!

MEASURE OR WEIGH YOUR FOOD UNTIL YOU BECOME FAMILIAR WITH PORTION SIZE. A level ½ cup of rice has only 70 Calories, but a heaping ½ cup contains 115 Calories.

SELECT FOOD PREPARATION METHODS TO REDUCE CALORIE CONTENT. For example, an egg fried in one teaspoon of butter contains 115 Calories, but a poached or hard-cooked egg contains only 80 Calories. Frying chicken or fish adds more Calories than baking or broiling. Preparing foods plain rather than adding sauces will also cut Calories.

CUT DOWN ON HIGH-FAT AND HIGH SUGAR FOODS. Remember than certain foods have more Calories than other foods, so you should eat smaller portions or fewer servings of these high Calorie foods. The Calories in apple pie aren't any more "fattening" than the Calories in an apple--there are just more of them!

USE A FOOD SUBSTITUTION PLAN. By substituting lower Calorie foods for higher Calorie foods, you may not have to reduce your food intake drastically. Listed in the following chart are some examples:

HIGHER CALORIE	MODERATE CALORIE
1 cup whole milk (160 Cal.)	1 cup 2% milk (120 Cal.)
1 slice apple pie (300)	1 baked apple (160)

½ cup canned pineapple
  heavy syrup (95)
1 tablespoon Blue Cheese
  salad dressing (75)
1 slice chocolate cake
  w/chocolate icing (235)
¼ cup ice cream (160)
Big Mac (563)
1 cup fruit yogurt (260)

½ cup canned pineapple in
  in juice (70)
1 tablespoon Miracle Whip
  salad dressing (55)
1 slice gingerbread (175)

¼ cup ice milk (100)
Quarter Pounder (454)
1 cup vanilla yogurt (200)

LOWER CALORIE
1 cup skim milk (80 Cal.)
1 medium apple (80)
¼ cup fresh pineapple (40)
1 tablespoon low-calorie French
  dressing (15)
1 slice angel food cake (135)
½ c. sherbet (70)
Regular hamburger (255)
1 cup plain yogurt (150)

Drink 5-6 glasses of water a day. This will help keep your system functioning well. It will also prevent loss of strength due to dehydration.

Keep a list of foods eaten each day and the number of calories consumed. This may help you stick to your weight loss program, particularly if you tend to nibble a lot. If you record everything you eat, you may think twice about sneaking an extra cookie or spoonful of ice cream!

Select foods for your daily menus from the Food Guide Pyramid and meet the requirements from each group so you get all the nutrients you need. Snacks and desserts should be chosen from the five main pyramid groups. Add foods from the Fats and Sweets Group only if you can afford the extra Calories.

These suggested patterns for meals will serve as a guide to help you plan your daily menus. The sample menus provide about 2,000 Calories and would meet the nutrient and energy needs of a male athlete who is trying to lose weight during the competitive season. A female athlete may wish to reduce the Calories to 1700. She could do this by drinking skim milk instead of 2% milk to save 140

Calories. At dinner she could use only one pat of margarine on the baked potato and substitute a slice of bread for the biscuit. These two changes would save 75 Calories. Eliminating either the apple or the chocolate chip cookie at snack time would save another 60 to 80 Calories.

SUGGESTED PATTERNS FOR MEALS	MENUS	
BREAKFAST:	BREAKFAST:	
Fruit	Orange juice (6 ounces)	90
Bread/Cereal/Egg (Choose 2)	1 cup cereal with	
Lowfat milk	½ cup 2% milk	170
	1 slice toast with	55
	1 teaspoon margarine	35
	1 cup 2% milk	120
		470 CAL
LUNCH	LUNCH	
Soup and crackers	Hamburger sandwich	
Sandwich	Meat patty (3 ounces)	250
Casserole (Choose 1 or 2)	Bun	120
Chef salad with	½ cup corn	50
low calorie dressing	1 medium banana	100
Yogurt	1 cup 2% milk	120
Fruits/Vegetables (Choose 1 or 2)		640 CAL
Lowfat milk		
DINNER:	DINNER:	
3 ounces serving meat	3 ounces baked chicken	220
Fruits/Vegetables (Choose 2 or 3)	Baked potato with	150
1 serving bread	2 teaspoons margarine	70
and butter	¼ cup green beans	15
1 serving milk	1 biscuit with	105
OR	1 teaspoon margarine	35
1 cup pasta or rice	¼ cup strawberries	35
casserole	1 cup 2% milk	120
Fruits/Vegetables (choose 2 or 3)		
1 serving milk		730 CAL
SNACKS:	SNACKS	
Use any remaining calories	2 cups unbuttered	
	popcorn	50
	1 apple	80
	1 chocolate chip cookie	60
		190 CAL

Fad Diets

In order to lose weight rapidly, many people are tempted to follow any diet that promises quick and easy weight loss. While there is a steady stream of new diets that offer promises of weight loss in only a few days, the fact is they don't work. If they did work, there wouldn't be so many fad diets.

Most fad diets produce initial results. However, the weight loss in almost all cases is water rather than fat. The main problem with fad diets is that they do nothing to change eating patterns. Fad diets tend to be either too complicated or too restrictive. These diets become a hassle to follow after a few weeks and most people can't stick with them for very long. After following the diet for so long, they resume their normal eating habits. Then all the weight they have lost goes right back on. Weight loss follows this yo-yo pattern for many people. They follow a fad diet, lose weight, gain the weight back, and then start all over again with another fad diet. This cycle of quick weight loss followed by rebound weight gain is not healthful.

Many popular "crash" diets not only are low in Calories, but also are low in nutrients. These diets may be based on eating just one food or one group of foods. Other crash diets also eliminate meals. You can and will lose weight on these diets because your caloric intake is so low. However, crash diets can be dangerous. If you are an athlete, you will not have enough energy for practice or competition. By drastically limiting your Calories, you are likely to become weak, irritable, and even ill. If you are still growing, your body will not get the nutrients it needs for growth.

Some of the more popular fad diets are low-carbohydrate diets or high-protein diets. These two types of diets are very similar. These diets allow very few, if any, carbohydrate foods such as breads, cereals, fruits, and vegetables. High protein foods, which may also be high in fat, are recommended in large amounts. Meat, poultry, fish, eggs, and cheese are the main foods that are eaten when following one of these diets.

Eliminating carbohydrates from the diet can make you feel sick. Weakness, fatigue, dizziness, headaches, and nausea are symptoms caused by lack of carbohydrate. Low carbohydrate diets are especially bad for athletes, because these diets cause weakness and dehydration. When you do not eat enough carbohydrate to provide energy for your body, the body then uses protein from lean muscle tissue for energy. As a result, you lose muscle rather than fat. Loss of muscle means loss of strength.

It takes time and discipline to lose weight. Beware of diets that promise a weight loss of more than two pounds per week. Also avoid diets that emphasize just one food or one particular type of food. When diets eliminate foods from certain food groups, important nutrients will be missing. Be suspicious of diets if you must purchase special products such as pills or supplements to replace foods. Activity Challenge II in the workbook will help you learn more about the dangers of fad diets and why you should avoid them. There is just no quick or easy way to lose weight safely!

Eating Disorders

People with eating disorders usually start with dieting to lose a few pounds because they are slightly overweight. However, once they start dieting, they can't seem to stop. Preoccupation with food, dieting, and thinness takes control of their lives.

Eating disorders are characterized by abnormal and obsessive eating behaviors. More women suffer from eating disorders than men because there is more pressure on females in our society to be thin. Athletes, both males and females, may develop eating disorders, especially, if they participate in "weight-related" activities such as wrestling, distance running, ballet, gymnastics, or figure skating. They think that competing at a low weight will help their performance or improve their appearance for competition.

Eating disorders have both physiological and psychological effects. If eating disorders are not treated, they can lead to illness and even death.

Anorexia nervosa is an eating disorder that is characterized by voluntary starvation. Anorexics usually think about food constantly and may be very hungry, but they do not eat except for very small portions. They also have a distorted idea about how they look. Even when they are very thin, they still think they are fat and need to lose more weight. Because anorexics have a fear of gaining weight, they often exercise excessively.

People with anorexia have severe health problems, depending on the degree of starvation and weight loss. As they lose fat and muscle tissue, they take on a skeleton-like appearance. Skin becomes dry and scaly, and hair starts falling out. Body functions also are affected. Heart rate and blood pressure decrease. Electrolyte balance is upset. Females are likely to lose their menstrual periods.

Many anorexics refuse to believe that they're sick. In severe cases of weight loss, they must be hospitalized and force- fed so that they will not starve. In addition to medical treatment, psychological counseling and family therapy are needed to help overcome the disease.

Bulimia is another eating disorder. Bulimia literally means "ox hunger." Bulimics will go on uncontrolled binges and consume large amounts of food in a short time. After stuffing themselves, they purge by vomiting or using laxatives so that they don't gain weight. Because of the behaviors that characterize this eating disorder, bulimia is often called the Binge/Purge Syndrome.

Although most bulimics are females, males may be bulimic, especially athletes who are dieting to reach a certain weight. When the diet becomes too restrictive they lose control, binge, and then purge so they don't gain weight. Weakness, fatigue, and dehydration can severely limit performance.

Bulimics have many health problems that are caused by purging. If forced vomiting is used for purging, the esophagus may become ulcerated due to the stomach acid in vomit. In severe cases, the esophagus may bleed and rupture. Dental cavities are also caused by excess acid. Sore throat, swollen glands, and facial puffiness also are caused by frequent vomiting. If laxatives are used, severe bowel problems may result. Electrolyte imbalances and possible heart beat abnormalities often affect bulimics and may be life threatening.

Bulimics generally recognize that their behavior is abnormal and are more likely to seek treatment than anorexics. Both medical and psychological treatment are needed to help the bulimic establish normal eating patterns and resolve health problems.

Gaining Weight

Gaining weight can be just as much of a problem for some athletes as losing weight is for others. For weight gain, energy input must be greater than energy output, which may be difficult to achieve if you're training hard and using up all the Calories you consume.

How can you develop a weight-control program that will result in weight gains? You will first want to have your body fat measured. Then you can monitor changes in your body composition. When you gain weight, you should gain muscle rather than fat. Well-developed muscles mean more strength and power for athletic activity. Since body fat does not contribute to muscular contractions during activity, weight gained in fat can hinder performance. To be sure that you are gaining muscle rather than fat, you will need to gain gradually, about one to two pounds per week. Plan ahead, since it is best to be at your desired competition weight by the beginning of your seaosn.

As with weight loss, the keys to a successful weight gain program are diet *and* exercise. Your diet must contain enough Calories both to maintain normal activity and to fuel muscle-building exercise. To add one pound of muscle per week you need 2,500 extra Calories, which is an increase of at least 350 Calories per day. If you have added more exercise and are training harder, you may need to increase your caloric intake by 500 Calories per day in order to gain one pound of muscle per week.

Also keep in mind that as you gain weight your basic caloric needs increase. Let's use Kevin as an example. Kevin weighed 165 at the beginning of his weight gain program. To meet his daily energy requirements at 165 pounds, he should have at least 22 Calories per pound, which is 3630 Calories a day. To gain one pound of muscle per week, he must have 350 to 500 *additional* Calories *each day* or 3980 to 4130 Calories.

After six weeks of weight training, Kevin weighs 170 pounds. To meet his daily energy requirements at his new weight of 170 pounds, he needs 3740 Calories per day (170 pounds x 22 Calories per pound). If Kevin wants to continue gaining weight, he now needs 4090 to 4240 Calories each day (3740 Calories + 350 to 500 Calories). If he does not keep increasing Calories to the necessary levels to maintain his new weight and to support additional muscle growth, Kevin will not be able to continue gaining weight.

You can use the basic diet as the core of your weight-gain diet. First determine the number of Calories necessary to meet your daily energy requirements. (See chart on page 84 in Chapter Six.) Then *add* the additional Calories you must have to meet your weekly weight gain goals. Choose your foods from the Food Guide Pyramid to meet your caloric and nutrient requirements. Just because you want to gain weight doesn't mean that you should be "hog-wild" and eat everything in sight! You will be able to eat the highest number of recommended servings from the Food Guide
pyramid and eat second helpings because of your higher caloric needs. Be sure to emphasize foods from the Bread, Vegetable, and Fruit Groups. These guidelines may also help you meet your weight gain goals:

EAT AT LEAST THREE OR MORE MEALS A DAY. You may find it easier to eat five or six small meals to reduce the amount of food you eat at one time, especially if your caloric requirements are extremely high.

EAT LARGER PORTIONS OR TAKE SECOND HELPINGS to increase your caloric intake.

EAT MORE COMPLEX CARBOHYDRATE FOODS. Carbohydrates, especially from the Bread and Cereal and Fruit and Vegetable Groups, provide premium fuel for weight gain. Carbohydrates supply the energy needed for muscle-building exercise. Without sufficient carbohydrate to burn for energy during exercise, your body may need to use some protein to help supply energy. Having enough carbohydrate in your diet "spares" protein so it can be used to build muscle.

Some athletes find it beneficial to use nutritionally balanced liquid meal supplements such as Ensure, Sustagen, and Exceed Nutritional Beverage. Liquid meals can be used to *supplement* daily caloric intake, especially if you have difficulty eating all the food that is needed for weight gain. Liquid meals are not a replacement for regular meals and should be used only as a supplement.

The food list below shows examples of good high carbohydrate foods to eat for meals and snacks.

HIGH CARBOHYDRATE FOODS	TOTAL CALORIES	CARBO CALORIES
Rice, 1 cup	233	198
Noodles, 1 cup	200	149
Bagel	160	123
Cheerios, 1 cup	110	80
Raisin bread, 1 slice	65	52
Baked potato, medium	145	131
Raisins, ¼ c.	120	118
Orange, medium	70	64
Vanilla yogurt, 1 cup	200	136
Exceed Nutritional Beverage	360	188

SNACK WISELY, USING FOODS FROM THE FOOD GUIDE PYRAMID. Rather than choosing only foods with empty calories, choose foods with some nutritional value. They supply nutrients you need. Choose milkshakes rather than soft drinks, sandwiches instead of salted snack foods, or pizza in place of doughnuts or pastries.

The suggested meal patterns given below serve as a guide in helping you plan your daily meals. These sample menus for a day provide about 4000 calories.

SUGGESTED PATTERNS FOR MEALS:

BREAKFAST:		BREAKFAST:	
Fruit		2 cups cereal	220
Bread/Cereal/Egg	(Choose 2 or more)	with 1 cup 2% milk	120
Milk		3 slices toast with	180
		3 teaspoons margarine	105
		and 3 teaspoons jam	55
		1 cup orange juice	180
			_____
			860 Cal

LUNCH:		LUNCH:	
Soup and crackers		2 tuna salad sandwiches	590
Sandwich		Carrot sticks	20
Casserole	(Choose 2 or 3)	1 apple	70
Yogurt		1 c. 2% milk	120
Chef salad and dressing		2 sugar cookies	110
Fruit/vegetables	(Choose 2 or 3)		_____
Milk			910 Cal

DINNER:		DINNER:	
2-3 cups pasta or rice casserole			
Fruits/vegetables	(Choose 2 or 3)		
Bread	(2 or more servings)		
Milk			
OR			
3 ounces meat (1 or 2 servings)		3 cups spaghetti with	
Fruits/vegetables	(Choose 2 or 3)	meat sauce	1000
Bread (2 or more servings)		Lettuce salad	20
Milk		with 2 Tablespoons	
		French dressing	140
		2 slices garlic bread	190
		1 cup 2% milk	120
		2 scoops ice milk	200
			_____
			1670 Cal

SNACKS:		SNACKS:	
Fruits	Peanut butter	1 cup low-fat yogurt	
Sandwiches	Nuts	with fruit	260
Breads	Dried fruits	2 oatmeal-raisin	
Ice cream	Cheese	cookies	130
Pudding	Yogurt	12 oz. grape juice	240
		1 banana	100
			730 Cal

The other part of a weight-gain program is exercise. If you just eat all those extra Calories and don't exercise, the only thing you'll gain is fat! To gain muscle, you must add a strength training program that will stimulate the muscles to use the extra Calories for growth.

It is the proper combination of diet and strength training that results in weight gain from larger and stronger muscles.

As with the weight loss program, you may want to weigh yourself once a week in the morning to check your progress. However, since the scale does not tell you if gains have been from fat or muscle, you should periodically have a skinfold test done so that you can compare your current body fat percentage with your pre-program level. If your weight gain has been in fat, your percent of body fat will have increased. If you body fat percentage has stayed the same or decreased, your gain has been in muscle mass.

There is no short cut to gaining weight. It takes *time* and *hard work*. Relying on a good diet and training program will give you results that last. Many athletes are tempted to use steroids to gain weight more rapidly. However, much of the muscle gained from steroid use does not last. This is because steroids cause the muscle tissues to retain a large amount of water. When steroid use is stopped, the muscle shrinks as water is lost. A high Calorie, high carbohydrate diet combined with proper strength training will help you make lasting strength gains.

Maintaining Weight

To maintain weight, energy input must equal energy output. Perhaps you're satisfied with your current weight and level of body fat--you're performing well and feeling strong. Then your job is easy. If you need 3,200 Calories per day for your basal needs, normal activities, and exercise, then you must consume 3,200 Calories. You don't have to worry about adding or subtracting Calories. You should also be using the Food Guide Pyramid as a guide for your food selection. To be sure you are maintaining your weight at the desired level, you may want to weigh about once a week. Periodic skinfold tests will tell you whether you may be gaining or losing body fat even though the scale shows a constant weight.

Remember that exercise is an important key to maintaining weight and body fat. If you reduce your exercise levels, you will have to reduce the amount of food you eat to maintain your input-output balance so that you don't gain. Likewise, if you are losing weight too rapidly, or if your body fat percentage is falling below recommended levels, you will need to increase your food intake to equalize your body's energy demands.

If you have been on a weight control program for gain or loss, you will be ready to go onto a weight maintenance plan once you have met your goal. The key will be learning to balance your energy input and output to maintain your new weight and level of body fat. Continue to monitor yourself by weighing and skinfold testing.

For best athletic performance you should be ready to begin maintaining your ideal weight at the *beginning* of your competitive season. If you have been on a weight loss program, you will be able to increase your caloric intake, which will provide extra energy to meet the demands of hard training uand competition. If you have been on an intensive strength training program for weight gain, you will not have as much time to spend lifting because of the extra demands of scheduled practices and competitions.

Designing a Personal Weight Control Program

Designing a personal weight control program involves several steps. First, determine your ideal weight. The best way to do this is by using body fat percentages. Is your goal to lose weight, gain weight, or maintain weight? Next, calculate how many pounds you need to lose or gain. Once you know what your target weight is, you must plan to create the necessary energy input/output balance to meet your weight goal. For either weight loss or weight gain, you will get best results with a combination of diet and exercise. The last step is to plan sample menus that you can follow to meet your caloric and nutrient requirements.

Activity Challenge III in the workbook will help you plan your own weight control program. By being able to use the basic principles of weight control, you should be able to develop an eating plan that can become a way of life.

CHAPTER SUMMARY--CASE STUDY

Re-read the Case Study that introduced this chapter. Using the information in this chapter, what advice would you give to Mrs. Johnson, Matt, and Jana?

1. Explain how determining body fat percentage would help both Matt and Jana determine their ideal weight.

2. Describe the relationship between energy input and energy output for weight loss and weight gain.

3. Answer Mrs. Johnson's questions about a weight loss program for Jana.

    How many pounds can Jana safely lose in one week?

    What is the minimum number of Calories that Jana should have per day when she is dancing on a regular basis?

    What is the best way for Jana to keep track of her weight loss?

4. Give four suggestions for making Calorie reductions in a weight loss program.

5. Why would it be dangerous for Jana to follow a fad diet?

6. Should Mrs. Johnson be concerned about Jana's developing an eating disorder? Explain your answer.

7. What type of food plan should Matt follow for gaining weight?

8. Why should Matt use a weight training program as part of his plan to gain weight?

9. Matt would like to gain ten pounds. If he wants to gain this weight properly, approximately how long should it take for him to reach his goal?

10. Why would it be best for Matt to have reached his goal weight *before* the beginning of football season?

9 PRE-COMPETITION MEALS--WHAT TO EAT BEFORE YOU COMPETE

CASE STUDY

I'm on the varsity swimming team. We compete in a lot of invitational meets on Saturdays, and I usually swim in three or four events. I try to eat something in the morning, but I don't want to eat too much because I'm afraid of getting sick. In between my events, I usually buy things like candy bars and soft drinks at the refreshment stand to keep me going until the end of the meet. One of my friends on the team told me that consuming sugary foods and beverages before I swim could hurt my performance. I really do need some advice about what to eat before I compete.

--Kim, high school senior

"I can't run unless I eat pancakes before a race." "I don't eat before a game; if I do, I get sick." Have you heard comments like these before? Just what should you eat before you compete?

There are no certain foods you should eat that will turn you into an automatic winner. However, eating the wrong foods may keep you from performing your best. The human body is a finely-tuned machine when at its peak performance level. Why compromise performance by selecting the wrong fuel? Since the pre-event meal is a special meal to prepare you for competition, special guidelines should be followed.

Purpose of the Pre-Competition Meal

Many athletes mistakenly think that all of their energy for competition comes from the pre-event meal. The main purpose of the pre-competition meal is to raise blood glucose to the proper level so that the body has energy to use at the beginning of competition. If you do not eat before competing, you may experience a premature lowering of blood glucose levels.

Most of the fuel for competition comes from glycogen, which your liver and muscles have stored from carbohydrate foods eaten the day or two before competition. During competition the glycogen that has been stored in the muscles is available to those muscles to use for energy. The glycogen that has been stored in the liver is reconverted into glucose, which is released into the blood stream. This glucose can then help maintain a constant supply of energy for the body throughout competition.

You do not want to start competition with low glucose and glycogen levels. Once you run out of these fuels, fatigue sets in rapidly. Marathoners call running out of fuel "hitting the wall." Skipping meals prior to competition will cause your glycogen supply to be dangerously low. Even though the pre-event meal can finish topping-off glycogen stores, it will not make up for skipped meals. The pre-event meal also helps prevent hunger during competition.

Guidelines for Pre-Competition Meals

What should you consider when planning your pre-competition meal? The main elements are timing, composition, and size of the meal. Because most athletes experience "butterflies" before competing, a small meal which is easily digested should be eaten three to four hours before the event. These guidelines will help you plan your pre-event meals:

1. EAT AT LEAST THREE TO FOUR HOURS BEFORE COMPETITION. This will allow your food to begin digesting and leave the stomach by game time. Foods remaining in the stomach may cause problems such as indigestion and nausea.
2. EAT FOODS THAT ARE HIGH IN CARBOHYDRATES. Carbohydrates are easy for the body to digest and will leave the stomach in two to four hours. Protein and fat are harder for the body to digest. Since they will not leave the stomach for five to six hours, foods containing protein and fat should be eaten in very small amounts at the pre-competition meal.

3. EAT ENOUGH TO BE SATISFIED AND PREVENT HUNGER. DON'T "PIG OUT"! A small meal of 500 to 800 Calories is easy for your stomach to handle and should keep you from feeling weak and hungry.
4. EAT FOODS THAT SETTLE WELL AND THAT YOU "BELIEVE IN." Everyone has personal preferences. What digests well for you may not settle well with someone else. Avoid foods that are highly spiced and those that tend to produce gas. Don't overlook the psychological importance of food giving you a "competitive edge."
5. BE SURE TO INCLUDE 2 TO 3 GLASSES OF FLUIDS WITH YOUR MEAL. This will help prevent dehydration. Ice water and fruit drinks are good. Some athletes avoid orange juice before competing, since the acid content may cause stomach upset. Fruit-*flavored* drinks such as Hi-C and Wyler's are good alternatives since they are high in carbohydrate and contain little of the high acid fruit juice. Avoid caffeinated beverages such as tea and coffee, particularly if you are not used to them. Caffeine is a stimulant and may cause a nervous athlete to become even more jittery. It's also best to stay away from carbonated beverages. The carbonation could cause gas formation in a "nervous" stomach.

Here are some suggestions for helping you plan your pre-competition meals:

INCLUDE THESE FOODS:	AVOID THESE FOODS:
Pastas (noodles, macaroni, spaghetti)	Highly salted or greasy foods (potato chips, corn chips, peanuts)
Bread/rolls/muffins with jelly	Fried foods (French fries, doughnuts)
Pancakes, French toast, waffles	Fatty meats (bacon, ham, steak)
Rice	Processed lunch meats (hot dogs, bologna)
Potatoes, especially baked or boiled	Peanut butter
Chicken noodle or rice soup	Mayonnaise
Canned fruits (peaches, pears, fruit cocktail, or applesauce)	Butter, cheese, high-fat dairy products
Gelatin, plain or with fruit	Caffeinated beverages
Plain cookies	Carbonated beverages
Angel food cake	
Fruit-flavored drinks	
Low-fat milk products	

The sample menus show how the recommended foods can be combined in meal planning. They may seem a little strange, but remember the main purpose of the pre-event meal is to digest easily.

SAMPLE MENUS
*Pre-event Meals Eaten 3-4 Hours Before Competing

Pancakes (or waffles or
  French toast)
Syrup
Canned peaches
Orange drink (Hi-C, etc.)

Jelly sandwich
Fruit cocktail
2 plain cookies
Fruit punch

*Avoid foods high in fat and protein

**Pre-event Meals Eaten 5-6 Hours Before Competing

Spaghetti (or noodle
  casserole or rice)
Gelatin salad with fruit
Bread with jelly
Angel food cake
Fruit punch or low-fat
  milk

Turkey or chicken sandwich
Baked potato with small
  amount of margarine
Pear or other fruit
2 or 3 raisin cookies
Grape drink or low-fat milk

**May include small amounts of foods containing fat and protein

If you use the concepts of timing, composition, and size when planning your pre-competition meals, it won't matter where you eat--at home, the school cafeteria, or a restaurant. Activity Challenges I and II in the workbook will help you apply what you have learned about pre-event meals. Several recipes are included after Activity Challenge II that you may wish to use.

Carbohydrate Loading

Carbohydrate loading is a way of getting the body to store two to three times the normal amount of glycogen in the muscles. By using a special diet plan and training routine, you trick your body into over-stocking carbohydrates.

Carbohydrate loading will not benefit all athletes. Normally the muscles can store enough carbohydrate to keep the body exercising for two hours. Carbohydrate loading offers no advantage in short sprint-type or throwing events and stop-start events such as volleyball, football, or basketball. Carbohydrate loading may benefit endurance athletes who participate in aerobic sports that are *continuous* for two hours or longer. For example, marathoners often will "carbo" load before important races.

Carbohydrate loading is a two-stage plan that lasts for one week. Stage One is called depletion. On Day 7, a week before competition, the athlete does exhaustive exercise to deplete muscle glycogen. The muscles that are used in competition are the muscles that must be depleted. Therefore, a runner must do a long run to deplete glycogen in the leg muscles. On Days 6, 5, and 4 the athlete exercises moderately and follows a diet that is low in carbohydrate and high in protein and fat. This combination of exercise and diet further depletes glycogen stores.

Stage Two is the carbohydrate loading phase. On Days 3, 2, and 1 the athlete does little or no exercise and follows a diet that is very high in carbohydrate (70% to 80%). The depleted muscles act like a dry sponge and soak up two to three times the normal amount of glycogen. On the day of competition, the athlete eats a small, high-carbohydrate meal three to four hours before competition.

Carbohydrate loading should be used no more than two or three times a year because it is hard on the body. During the depletion phase, athletes often experience extreme fatigue, headaches, and nausea. If an athlete has a history of heart problems or diabetes, carbohydrate loading can cause severe health problems. Another side effect is weight gain. During the three day carbohydrate loading stage additional water is stored along with the glycogen.

If you have to compete several times in one or two days, such as in a tournament, you may want to try a modified carbohydrate-loading plan. The depletion stage of the original carbohydrate-loading plan is eliminated and only the carbohydrate loading stage is used. This shortened, three day version helps replace the glycogen you have used in training and insures a good supply of glycogen for competition. The best thing is that it does not cause the unpleasant side-effects and can be used as frequently as desired. Chart 9-1 [5] shows how this modified "carbo" loading plan works.

---

[5] Based on information from Sherman, W. M. et al: Effect of exercise-diet manipulation on muscle glycogen and its subsequent utilization during performance. International Journal of Sports Medicine. May, 1981, pp. 114-118.

DAY 1	Moderate training	High Carbohydrate Diet
DAY 2	Moderate training	High Carbohydrate Diet
DAY 3	Little or no training	High Carbohydrate Diet
COMPETITION DAY	High Carbohydrate Pre-event Meal	

A high pre-exercise level of glycogen is beneficial because it allows you to exercise for longer periods by delaying fatigue. However, carbohydrate loading is not necessary for most athletes. A high carbohydrate meal the night before competition will fill up glycogen stores. This is a good time to eat spaghetti, macaroni and cheese, or a noodle casserole. Then eat a small, high carbohydrate pre-event meal to top-off glycogen stores and raise your blood sugar to the proper level. This eating plan should provide plenty of energy for most competitions.

Eating "On-the-Run"

Often during multi-session competitions such as wrestling matches, track, gymnastic, and swimming meets, an athlete must snack or eat a small meal to prevent hunger and weakness. Therefore, if you compete in these sports, you may need to consider packing a snack or a brown-bag meal.

When eating between sessions, try to follow these guidelines:

1. Allow *at least* two hours between eating and competition time. This will help your food to begin digesting properly.
2. Eat lightly, just enough to take the "edge" off your hunger.
3. Include fluids, preferably ice water. This will help prevent dehydration, which could hurt your performance.

Foods packed as snacks and for brown-bag meals should be high in carbohydrate, since they will digest easily and quickly. Listed below are foods that are recommended for eating on the run:

Bagels	Fruit snack packs
Hard rolls	Fresh fruits (ones you digest well)
Rice cakes	Fruit juices

Cereal (Raisin Squares, Chex, etc.)	Ice water
Graham crackers	Exceed© Fluid Replacement and Energy Drink
Animal crackers	Liquid meal supplements (Exceed©
Jelly sandwich	Sports Nutrition Supplement,
Low-fat yogurt	Ensure©,SustaCal©, Sustagen©)

When packing foods to take with you, or if you are purchasing foods at a refreshment stand, avoid these foods that tend to be high in fat and protein content:

Fried and/or salted snack foods (potato chips, corn chips, French fries, doughnuts)
Hot dogs and lunch meats such as bologna
Peanut butter
Mayonnaise on sandwiches
Caffeinated beverages
Carbonated beverages

Liquid Meal Supplements

Many athletes who have difficulty eating solid food before competition have found that liquid meal supplements are just the thing for them. Exceed© Sports Nutrition Supplement is a liquid meal supplement that has been developed especially for athletes. This product can be purchased in many sporting goods stores. Ensure©, SustaCal©, and Sustagen© are products that were originally developed for hospital patients who could not eat solid food. These brands are usually sold in drug stores. Liquid meals usually come in several flavors such as vanilla, chocolate, and strawberry. They generally taste best when they are chilled.

Liquid meals have several advantages. Most are pre-mixed and sold in cans, so they are very easy to pack in a travel bag. These meals are easily digested because they are high in carbohydrate. Since they leave the stomach rapidly, liquid meals can be used as close as two hours before competition. They also help contribute to an athlete's fluid needs.

Be sure to use one of the recommended brands as a pre-event meal. Do not use powdered breakfast drinks or reducing-formula meals. Their nutrient composition is different from that of the recommended brands, and they could cause stomach upset.

Don't wait to try a liquid meal supplement on the day of your most important competition of the season. Experiment during training to find what agrees with you. You can try various flavors and drinking different amounts. A liquid meal beverage many be an ideal pre-competition meal or snack for you.

Sugar Before Competition

If you are looking for "quick energy" before you compete, *Udon't* run to the nearest vending machine or refreshment stand for a candy bar or soft drink! Eating sugary foods or drinking beverages containing sugar an hour or less before you compete may have just the opposite effect.

When you eat or drink anything containing sugar, the pancreas releases insulin into the blood stream to help your body use the carbohydrate. This release of insulin has little noticeable effect when you are not active. However, once you start exercising, your muscles become more sensitive to the insulin and there may be a rapid drop in the blood sugar level. This condition is called *hypoglycemia* or low blood sugar. When your blood sugar level drops too low, you may become light-headed, weak, and uncoordinated. As a result, your performance can suffer. To be on the safe side, foods and beverages, except water, should not be consumed less than an hour before competing.

Food Logs

Many athletes have found it beneficial to keep a food log or diary. This can help determine whether poor performances are related to foods consumed prior to practices or competition. On days when you do not feel well, list the foods that you ate, when you ate, and the symptoms you experienced. By doing this you will develop a list of foods that you should avoid before practice sessions or games. Likewise, you may wish to note in your log the foods you ate and when you ate on days that you performed well. A log sheet can be designed to look something like this:

DATE	FOODS CONSUMED	WHEN FOODS WERE EATEN	SYMPTOMS

You are an experiment of one. Remember that eating the *wrong* foods before competition may keep you from performing your best. Take the time to find the winning combination of foods that works best for you!

CHAPTER SUMMARY--CASE STUDY

Re-read the Case Study that introduced this chapter. Using the information in this chapter, what advice would you give Kim?

1. Explain the purposes of the pre-event meal to Kim.

2. Why is it important for Kim not to skip meals a day or two prior to competitions?

3. Give Kim five guidelines to use in planning pre-competition meals.

4. Discuss carbohydrate loading with Kim.
    What is the purpose of carbohydrate loading?

    Describe the differences between the original one week carbohydrate loading plan and the three day modified plan.

    Explain which plan you would recommend if Kim wants to try "carbo" loading.

What are liquid meal supplements?

Why might Kim want to use a liquid meal as a pre-event snack?

5. Kim's school is hosting a big invitational swim meet on Saturday. Kim is scheduled to swim a qualifying heat in the 100 meter butterfly at 11:30 AM.
    Plan a pre-competition meal for Kim.

    At what time should Kim eat?

6. Give Kim three guidelines to follow when eating between events at swimming meets.

7. Suggest five things to pack as a "brown bag meal" so that Kim doesn't have to buy food and beverages at the refreshment stand.

8. Explain to Kim why consuming soft drinks and candy bars too close to competition could interfere with performance.

9. Why would Kim find it helpful to start keeping a food log?

10 WATER--A MATTER OF LIFE OR DEATH

CASE STUDY

This will be my first year running cross country. To get into shape I've been running about four miles a day, but I have problems training in the summer heat. Occasionally I get "goosebumps" when I run and become extremely thirsty. I'm afraid to drink too much because I don't want water sloshing around in my stomach. I've seen ads for sports drinks, so maybe these would help. What can I do to prevent having heat problems when I run? Would sports drinks be good for me to use?

--Leslie, high school freshman

Of all the nutrients your body needs, water is the most essential for survival. You can live without food for days, even for weeks and months. But death comes rapidly, in a matter of a few days, if you're deprived of water. About 60% of you body weight is water. If normal and healthy, the body maintains water at a constant level.

Functions of Water

Almost all of the body's living cells need water to perform their functions. Water carries the necessary nutrients to the cells and carries waste materials from the cells. Water is also used in the conversion of food into energy. Digestion, absorption, and transportation of nutrients all depend on water. The body utilizes water as a solvent for eliminating waste products, which if allowed to accumulate, could build to toxic levels. Water is an essential component of all body fluids. Blood plasma, for example, is about 92% water. Some body fluids work as lubricants. They keep body tissues such as the eyes and air passages moist and cushion the joints and internal organs. Water also serves as a coolant for maintaining proper body temperature.

Water Balance

Since water is involved in so many body functions, proper water balance is essential. Proper water balance is maintained when you take in the same amount of water that you lose. This daily input-output balance involves about ten cups of water.

Thirst is one way that the body signals its need for fluids. The hypothalamus, located in the brain, tells you when you need more water. However, you cannot always depend on your thirst center; you may sometimes need to drink more than your thirst indicates. For adequate water intake you should drink six to eight cups of liquids each day. This total can include other beverages besides water. Foods also contain water. Milk is 87% water, apples and oranges are about 85% water, and cooked meats, about 50% water. Even foods that you might describe as dry contain some water. For example, breads and cereals may contain 8 to 35% of their weight in water. In addition to water from food and fluid intake, your body produces about 20% of its water supply. When carbohydrates and fats are burned for energy, the main by-products involved in this chemical reaction are energy and water. This water is known as metabolic water.

Your body is so efficient that it uses the water it needs and them eliminates the rest. The largest amount of water is excreted as urine by the kidneys. The body also loses water through the skin in order to maintain normal body temperature. Even at rest you perspire, but you probably are not aware that it is happening. This type of water loss is called *insensible* perspiration. However, when you become more active, water loss though the skin intensifies. Perspiration becomes noticeable because your skin feels wet. Finally, air exhaled from the lungs accounts for some loss of body water.

Water Distribution and Electrolytes

Besides the water input/output balance, water distribution inside the body is crucial. Basically there are two "compartments" where water is found. Water found inside the cells is known as *intra*cellular water and water found outside the cells is knwon as *extra*cellular water.

This distribution of water in the intracellular and extracellular compartments is primarily regulated by minerals called *electrolytes*. They are called electrolytes because they have an electrical charge. The most important electrolyte minerals are potassium, sodium, and chlorine.

Potassium, which has a positive charge, is found mainly in the intracellular water. Potassium is used for biochemical reactions that take place in the cells. Sodium and chloride (a form of chlorine) are found mainly in the extracellular water. Sodium has a positive charge and chloride has a negative charge. These two minerals are used in regulating the acid-base balance of the body. Sodium also works with potassium to help transmit nerve impulses.

Electrolytes have an important role in regulating water movement in and out of the cells. Water can be moved through the cell walls by a process called *osmosis*. The concentration of electrolytes inside and outside of the cells creates osmotic pressure, which moves fluids either in or out of the cells. This movement allows for a well-regulated exchange of nutrients and waste products. Therefore, the relationship of electrolytes and body water is important for athletic performance.

Water and Temperature Regulation

The most important fact you should remember about water is that it cools your body to maintain a normal temperature. During physical activity, the body produces a great amount of heat as it burns nutrients for energy. As your temperature increases, you begin to sweat so that your body doesn't overheat.

To produce sweat, you must have an adequate supply of body water. Drinking before, during, and after activity is the only way to maintain the proper water level. The second part of the cooling process is evaporation; the sweat must evaporate from your skin for cooling to occur. If you exercise in hot, humid weather, you may "drip" sweat. Instead of evaporating, the sweat falls to the ground and you miss the cooling action. Heavy clothing and equipment can also interfere with sweat evaporation. To prevent such problems, avoid exercising during the middle of the day. Early morning and late evening hours are the coolest. Work to build up your tolerance to the heat if you must exercise in hot, humid conditions. It will take about two weeks to become acclimatized, and even then you must use extreme caution. Keep as much skin exposed as possible, so that sweat can evaporate. Mesh jerseys or cut-off T-shirts, lightweight shorts, and cut-off socks are preferable to full gear in hot weather.

Dehydration and Hyperthermia

What happens when your cooling system breaks down? Not having enough water in your body before beginning to exercise or replacing water during activity can cause dehydration. Even if you lose only a couple of pounds of body weight as sweat, you will not be able to work at your top performance levels. If insufficient water is available, the muscle cells become less efficient at producing energy, and peformance suffers. Loss of water will also increase heart rate, raise blood pressure, and elevate body temperature. Without careful attention to dehydration, heat illness (hyperthermia) may occur. Problems may vary from temporary heat cramps to death from heat stroke.

You should learn how to recognize the symptoms of hyperthermia and know how to give first-aid treatment. You cannot afford to ignore the heat problems caused by dehydration or other breakdowns in the body's cooling system. There are three forms of heat illness: heat cramps, heat exhaustion, and heat stroke.

Heat Cramps

Heat cramps are often the first sign of dehydration. Loss of water can cause painful muscle spasms in the thigh and calf muscles. Other symptoms indicating the onset of dehydration and overheating include chills accompanied by "goosebumps" and clammy skin. The sensation of thirst may also alert you to potential problems. If you experience any of these symptoms, you should replace lost body water by drinking about four to six ounces (½ to ¾ cup) of water every 10 to 15 minutes. Remove as much clothing as possible to allow sweat to evaporate and cool the body. Rest in a shaded place until the symptoms disappear. If you resume activity after experiencing any of these symptoms, be sure to monitor yourself carefully for recurring heat problems.

Heat Exhaustion

The second form of heat illness is heat exhaustion. The symptoms of heat exhaustion are more severe than those associated with heat cramps. A loss of 5 to 10% of an athlete's body weight in water may trigger heat exhaustion, especially if the athlete is not well-conditioned or is not acclimatized to heat and humidity. You can learn to recognize heat exhaustion by a variety of symptoms. Extreme weakness and fatigue may be accompanied by headache and dizziness. Reduced sweating, due to a lack of water, will cause an elevation in body temperature. Upon noticing these symptoms, you should stop exercising immediately and move to a cool place. Continue the cooling process by removing as much clothing as possible and placing cold, wet towels over the body. A cold shower could be used instead of towels. Fluid replacement is critical. Drink cool or cold water as soon as possible. Then continue to replace fluids by drinking two cups of water for every pound you have lost.

Heat Stroke

Heat stroke is a medical emergency and a life-or-death situation! One of the major problems with heat stroke is that it can occur suddenly; some of the symptoms may overlap with those associated with heat cramps and heat exhaustion. Staggering, visual disturbances, confusion, and even hallucinations are symptomatic. The skin becomes hot and dry and body temperature rises rapidly. Complete collapse and unconsciousness may happen in severe cases. *Call for medical help immediately!* Preventing serious injury or death requires *lowering body temperature immediately.* A temperature of 106°F or above for more than a few minutes will begin to cause damage to the brain, kidneys, and liver. If immediate action is not taken, death can occur. Until medical help arrives, cool the body using any available means. Remove clothing and use ice packs, iced towels, or a cold tub bath to lower body temperture. Hospitalization may be necessary.

Preventing Dehydration

By understanding the role of water in controlling body temperature, you can prevent heat illness by avoiding dehydration. As a preventive measure drink plenty of water both before and during activity. Drink 1 ½ to 2 cups of water 15 to 30 minutes before practice or competition. Continue to drink small amounts (about ½ cup) about every 15 minutes throughout practice or competition. You may even need to drink more frequently under hot, humid conditions.

The main concern is to have your body absorb fluids as rapidly as possible. Several factors influence the rate of absorption. One

140

of these is temperature. Cold drinks leave the stomach more rapidly than those which are warm. In addition, cold fluids help cool the body internally. Sugar content of fluids also affects the absorption rate. Any fluids that contain sugar are not absorbed as quickly, since the sugar must first be digested, so it is advisable to drink only water during competition. Even though larger amounts of fluid empty more rapidly from the stomach than small amounts, drinkng too much at once may cause a "sloshing" sensation. To avoid this, take small dirnks more frequently--about 4 ounces (approximately ¾ of a styrofoam cup) every 15 minutes.

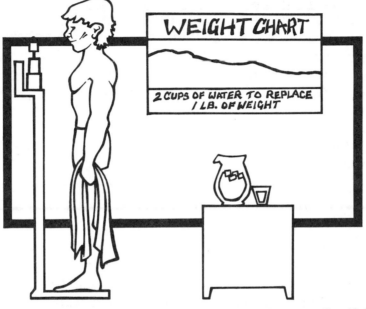

Illus. 10-1

At one time coaches withheld water from their athletes during practices or competitions because they thought drinking water would cause stomach cramps. Research has shown that the body cannot adapt to dehydration. Even if you lose only two to three percent of your body weight in water, your capacity for work is reduced. You will always perform better if you are properly hydrated during physical activity.

After practice or competition you should continue to replace water losses, even though you may not feel thirsty. You cannot rely on thirst to tell you how much water is needed. You may fe el fully rehydrated but still need water. As shown in Illustration 10-1 the best way to monitor fluid needs is to weigh yourself before and after you exercise. For every pound you have lost (primarily water rather than fat), you need to drink two cups of fluid. If you lose four pounds on a hot afternoon, you will rehydrate properly by consuming eight cups (½ gallon) of fluid. You do not have to rely solely on water to meet all your fluid replacement requirements. After exercise cold beverages such as fruit juices, lemonade, sports drinks, and milk are fine. Don't rely totally on coffee, tea, or colas for fluid replacement. They contain caffeine, which tends to deplete the body water supply by increasing urine production.

Forced Dehydration

Unfortunately some athletes, especially wrestlers, use forced dehydration to lose weight. Instead of following a sensible weight control program to lose body fat, they "pig-out" until two days before a match. Then they try to make weight by using a variety of methods that cause dehydration. Even though they begin drinking immediately after weigh-ins, dehydration cannot be corrected in the short time prior to competition.

Rapid weight loss by dehydration reduces performance levels by causing premature fatigue. Athletes also face the risk of heat exhaustion, irregular heart function, and circulatory collapse. If you have used dehydration as a weight-loss technique, you should think about the dangers before continuing this practice!

Sports Drinks

Look in almost any sports magazines and you will find advertisements for sports drinks. Some advertisements suggest that sports drinks are better than water. Others make claims that they will improve performance. Just what are you to believe?

The most important ingredient in sports drinks is the water they contain. Remember the basic purpose of sports drinks is to replace body fluids lost during exercise. If you look at the ingredient label of sports drinks you'll notice that they also contain varying amounts of carbohydrates.

For most athletes the main concern is that a replacement beverage should get water into circulation as soon as possible. Many sports drinks, including Gatorade© and Quickick©, contain sugars such as glucose and sucrose. Most sports drinks have a carbohydrate concentration ranging from 5 to 8 percent to allow for fluid absorption into the blood stream. Too much sugar in a sports drink will cause the fluid to stay in the stomach much longer than plain water. Check the label on a sports drink for the caloric content of an 8 ounce serving. Fifty to 70 Calories will provide a carbohydration in the proper range for good fluid absorption. Also check the label to see if a sports drink contains fructose. You may want to avoid sports drinks that contain fructose as the *main* carbohydrate source since fructose may cause diarrhea.

Glucose polymers are a new type of carbohydrate source being used in several sports drinks. Exceed© Fluid Replacement and Energy Drink and Max© are sports drinks that contain glucose polymers. A glucose polymer is a string of sugar molecules that has the effect of providing more carbohydrate without affecting fluid absorption rate. The body "sees" a string of sugar molecules the same way it looks at one sugar molecule--as one unit. Since glucose polymers are larger than sugar molecules, they provide more carbohydrates. Glucose polymer drinks can have a carbohydrate concentration of up to 10 percent or even more without interfering with water absorption.

How necessary is it to replace carbohydrate during exercise? The answer to this question depends on how long and how hard you exercise. The body's normal carbohydrate stores last about two hours, which should cover most workouts and competitions. However, research studies on endurance athletes show that consuming a carbohydrate-containing sports drink may delayfatigue. Marathoners and triathletes may find that a sports drink is beneficial. For most athletes, sports drinks are no real improvement over water.

Be aware that if you use sports drinks wrong, they can work against you. You may want to avoid using sports drinks 60 to 30 minutes before competition. Because of the carbohydrate content, sports drinks could cause hypoglycemia (low blood sugar) in some athletes who are "sugar-sensitive." When you drink or eat anything containing sugar, your pancreas releases insulin to help your body use the carbohydrate. However, exercise causes you to become more sensitive to the insulin, and your blood sugar level drops. A person who is sugar-sensitive may experience weakness and feel uncoordinated once they begin to excercise. Therefore, drinking water in the hour before practice or competition will prevent this type of reaction from occuring.

Since everyone is different, you need to experiment with different products. Compare the sports drinks that contain glucose and sucrose to those that contain glucose polymers. Try drinking different amounts and at different times during exercise. Keep in mind that sports drinks taste best during and after exercise. Activity Challenge I in the workbook will help you evaluate several different sports drinks.

Electrolyte Replacement

Many sports drinks also contain small amounts of electrolyte minerals to replace those that are lost in sweat. Sweat is mainly water with small amounts of sodium, chlorine, and potassium. Even though you sweat heavily, you do not deplete your body's stores of electrolytes. As you sweat, the concentration of electrolytes in your body actually increases. This happens because you lose proportionally more water than electrolytes. Therefore, during exercise it is more important to replace water than it is to replace electrolytes.

How can you replace the small amounts of electrolyte minerals that you do lose? Foods in a normal diet can easily replace these losses. Eating a banana or drinking a glass of orange juice will replace any potassium you may have lost. Sodium can be replaced by adding an extra shake of salt to your food or by eating pretzels or crackers as a snack. Even though hot weather can suppress your appetite, it is important to eat regular meals. The foods you eat help replace the water and elctrolyte minerals necessary for fluid balance.

Avoid using salt tablets to replace the salt lost in sweat. Your main concern is water replacement, not salt replacement. In fact, high concentrations of salt upset the balance of intracellular and extracellular water. Because salt tablets increase the sodium concentration in the extracellular fluids, water from inside the cells crosses over the membranes to dilute the high sodium levels. This decrease in intrcellular water can make existing dehydration problems much worse. Salt tablets can also irritate the lining of the stomach and could cause vomiting. To prevent problems such as these, don't take salt tablets! If you do, be sure to take them with *plenty* of water.

Water is often called the forgotten nutrient. For athletes it is the nutrient most critical for top performance, Don't make the mistake of overlooking its importance!

CHAPTER SUMMARY--CASE STUDY

Re-read the Case Study that introduced this chapter. Using the information in this chapter, what advice would you give Leslie?

1. Explain to Leslie why the body needs water.
   Discuss how water is used to regulate body temperature.

   What happens when there is not enough water to cool the body?

2. The "goosebumps" and thirst that Leslie experienced when running in the heat were symptoms of which stage of hyperthermia?

3. Give Leslie several suggestions for preventing dehydration.

4. Explain to Leslie why it is better to use weight rather than thirst as an indicator of fluid replacement.
   Leslie loses three pounds while running, how much replacement fluid is needed?

5. Describe the ingredients that are found in sports drinks.

6. Give Leslie several recommendations for using sports drinks most effectively.

7. What is the best way for Leslie to replace electrolytes that are lost in sweat?

INDEX